50 ideas

you really need to know

the future

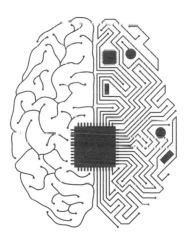

Richard Watson

Quercus

Contents

Introduction

The future is unwritten, but how we imagine it to be can influence present attitudes and behaviours, much in the same way that our individual and collective histories can define who we are and how we act, as most psychoanalysts will tell you. In other words, both past and future are always present.

But the future is not distributed equally. Science laboratories, research establishments and academic institutions create and explore new ideas long before they become widely available or fashionable elsewhere. Much the same might be said of younger people, who are often more open to experimenting with new ideas and less invested in, or constrained by, the frameworks of existing thinking.

What you will find inside this book is a selection of 50 ideas from the frontiers of futures thinking, along with some quotes and illustrative timelines. Some of these, and some of the people behind them, might seem a little crazy. But then who, without the benefit of 20/20 hindsight, can tell? Maybe that's the whole point about thinking of the future. It's not a matter of people being right or wrong, but is, rather, a way of inspecting our beliefs. It's a way of disrupting the present and unearthing our assumptions about what can and cannot happen – assumptions that are always embedded in our thinking about the future. Also, it's a way of reminding people of the oft-forgotten fact that the future is shaped by our present choices and actions.

Most importantly, engaging with the future gives us all the permission to dream. Two other aspects are apparent about the future. The first is that technology tends to act as an accelerant. Second, we often overestimate the impact of technological and social change in the shorter term, while underestimating it over much longer periods.

You may doubt this, but that's possibly because the future tricks us by wearing a disguise and showing up unannounced. The future trickles into our daily lives, usually without warning or fanfare. If, instead, the future arrived all at once, to the sound of distant drums, we would no doubt be either rather alarmed or pleasantly impressed.

My hope is that the pages that follow will do a bit of both.

01 Ubiquitous surveillance

George Orwell was right. He just got the date wrong. It's reported that there are now 32 CCTV cameras within 180m (200 yards) of the author's former home at 27B Canonbury Square in North London. In total, there are more than 4 million CCTV cameras in the UK – one for every 14 citizens. The average Brit appears on screen 300 times every day and this trend is becoming observable elsewhere.

The UK is at the forefront of a global shift in surveillance, and CCTV (closed-circuit television) is only the beginning. In the UK, anyone arrested in connection with a suspected crime has his or her DNA added to a database, where it stays, indefinitely, whether or not the person is found guilty of any wrongdoing. In 2009, the UK government attempted to gain approval for another database that would record in real time the electronic communications of every individual and make the data available to 653 British organizations. That's every single email, phone call, Google search and credit card transaction. The plan was shelved, but it resurfaced in 2012 under new anti-terror laws, the only real difference being that the information would be held, in the first instance, by landline, mobile phone and broadband providers.

The rest of Europe isn't far behind. A paper emanating from the Advisory Group on the Future of European Home Affairs, for instance, suggests monitoring: 'Every object the individual uses, every transaction they make and almost everywhere they go.' This could include tax details, employment records, banking details, credit card use, health records,

timeline

1932	1949	1973	2005	2012
Brave New World is published	*Nineteen Eighty-four* is published	First CCTV camera appears in Times Square	National rollout of automatic number plate recognition system in UK	Kids' smartphone apps that spy on locations and harvest photographs

travel history and even membership of social networks. Meanwhile, in India, the government has just embarked on a ten-year plan to create the world's largest identity database. In theory, this is a good idea, because it will help the government to provide essential services, but history would suggest that uses for this information will multiply, along with the growth of data analytics – and that the government will get considerably more out of the relationship than the citizens.

Then there are seemingly innocent items such as store loyalty cards – private surveillance under the banner of loyalty points essentially. One major company proudly admits to owning 40 terabytes of information about the habits of 24 million individual customers.

Looking forward So what might surveillance look like in the future? RFID (Radio-Frequency Identification) tags might allow local

> **In the Huxleyan prophecy, Big Brother does not watch us, by his choice. We watch him, by ours. There is no need for wardens or gates or Ministries of Truth.**
>
> **Neil Postman,** author and media critic

They Know, you know

Ubiquitous surveillance is often assumed to mean CCTV cameras poking in peoples' faces and this is indeed true, although in the future the cameras will include those attached to privately owned mobile phones featuring face recognition technology. So if you're lying on a beach somewhere in the future, someone you don't know might point a phone at you, find out who you are, then work out where you're from. If you've told others about your future plans via social networks, criminals might access this information then tell someone to visit your home and rob you.

2015	2019	2020	2025
'Black boxes' become mandatory in all new cars in USA	Malicious intent detectors in most public spaces	Billions of dot-sized cameras are everywhere	Governments hold DNA samples of every citizen worldwide

councils and authorities to monitor domestic dustbin usage, alerting them when incorrect items are placed in recycling bins. As for CCTV cameras, there is very little evidence that they reduce crime. What they do instead is catch criminals in the act and reassure people looking for certainty and control in an age that is becoming more uncertain and complex.

But even these measures are being overtaken by ideas borrowed more from science fiction than from your local hardware store. Biometric products are already being introduced for use with mobiles and we may one day see voice, fingerprint, palm print and iris recognition entry systems in our own homes due to a perceived need for added security plus the falling cost of such technologies. Kwikset, America's leading lock company, for example, has created a domestic fingerprint entry system. And don't think you're safe at work either: 75 per cent of US companies monitor employees' email and 30 per cent track keystrokes and the amount of time employees spend on their computer. Monitoring employee activity isn't new, but it is becoming more pervasive thanks to digital technologies that make activities easier to capture, store and search.

Other by-products of the computer age that go unnoticed include mobile phones, most of which now contain cameras, which may one day be linked to face recognition technology. On top of that, people are increasingly choosing to communicate with each other through digital interfaces, which leave a digital trace.

Nothing is private As a consequence, we can now look very closely at things that were previously unobservable. For example, the UK government has plans to centralize the records of the National Health Service to allow social services to monitor every single child in Britain. In the future this could include looking at which toys parents are spending money on or how many portions of fruit a child is likely to be eating each day.

Similarly, insurance companies may one day be able to monitor their customers and deny them insurance cover based on observed behaviour. According to Narayanan Kulathuramaiyer, an expert in this area, companies involved in the collection of such data are selling it to government agencies: 'At a level you would not even imagine.'

Privacy in a digital age

If you're walking around with a phone switched on, you're already broadcasting your presence to others. In the future your phone will replace your wallet, your diary and eventually your house keys. Such devices will therefore collect a host of useful digital memories that will help future governments and law-enforcement agencies piece together a compelling picture of who you are and what you think, based upon your geographical movements, relationships with others and purchasing patterns. But it doesn't end there. Malicious intent detectors attempt to predict future behaviour based on body language, remote body-temperature readings and eye movement. These devices are already being used by the Department of Homeland Security in the USA, as are automated number plate recognition systems and facial recognition systems in crowds.

This is just the tip of the iceberg. In 2002, the Pentagon in the USA sought funding for a programme called Total Information Awareness, the aim of which was to identify 'suspicious behaviour' using data-mining techniques. Funding was refused, but parts of the project have survived. The UK, China, France, Israel and Germany are thought to have similar programmes.

In theory, this could be a good thing, and most people seem eager to give up a little individual liberty in return for the promise of collective security. But governments have a terrible record of keeping records secret. Once a new technology is in place, its uses tend to expand.

the condensed idea
Big Brother *is* watching

02 Digital democracy

'Government of the people by the people.' Really? Democracy was designed to represent the views of the people. But it soon evolved into mediation by a cast of thousands, ranging from unelected officials and advisors to professional lobbyists. Unless they had serious time or money to spare, solitary individuals were rarely able to shape the debate or challenge those in power. But this is changing.

Ubiquitous connectivity means that it is now a practical proposition to ask more of the people more of the time. This doesn't necessarily mean continuous referenda, but it does represent a credible threat to the legitimacy of some of those who claim to act on the people's behalf. After all, if a national government can instantly connect with its people, why bother with hoards of intermediaries? (Press 1 followed by # if you agree, press 2 followed by # if you don't or if you would like to speak to an advisor simply hold.)

Digitalization means that governments will need to listen to citizens more carefully in the future because more ordinary voters will be able to create, transmit and comment upon policy ideas without the need for local party membership, professional lobbyists, PR campaigns, television ads or direct mail campaigns. Similarly, more politicians will use Web 2.0 tools to run ads on YouTube, gather micro-donations via PayPal, or use mobile phones to organize instant protests against rivals. It also means that voting in supermarkets, in McDonald's and on the bus will all be possible and perhaps even encouraged in the future.

timeline

2011	2016	2018	2019
Voters identify local problems using Google maps	Careless tweet leads to downfall of US President	eBay-style ratings of all government services	Governments stop writing material down for fear of disclosure

> **❝The political technology of the industrial age is no longer appropriate technology for the new civilization taking form around us. Our politics are obsolete.❞**
>
> **Alvin Toffler, author of *Future Shock***

The up side The hope is that developments such as these will make politics more interesting and politicians more accountable and honest. Gone will be the days of utterances made in small rooms 'off the record' in the full knowledge that such remarks will not be captured by a television news crew. Nowadays, thanks to mobile devices, the media is always present. This means we will be able to check the accuracy of politicians' promises against what's been said before, and alert others to any dishonesty – and this is very good news. Politicians have historically been masters of manipulating facts, and the traditional media, especially television, encouraged this. Politicians could covertly hide behind an altered image and some edited remarks. Not in the future. Global connectivity demands instant authenticity and promotes radical transparency. The media is everyone.

As one Syrian activist called Khaled said in a *Financial Times* interview: 'The regimes thought the youth were divorced from politics. They didn't notice that young people were connected among themselves.'

The Internet has changed peoples' lives significantly over a relatively short time, but most notable may be its ability to aggregate opinion instantly, an application that is ideally suited to the democratic process. Moreover, there is no reason why online aggregation should be limited to a single nation. If the whole world has access to digital tools, why can't the whole world vote on important issues such as climate change? Why would this newfound power be limited to local politics? Why can't we all vote for the European President or the United Nations Secretary General using whatever digital tool is close at hand?

2020	2022	2023	2025
Voting in McDonald's ('would you like a vote with those fries?')	X Factor producer brought in to advise on MEP election	Facebook 'likes' legally accepted as voting	All political advertisements targeted to audiences of just one

> **‘There is a connection waiting to be made between the decline in democratic participation and the explosion in new ways of communicating.’**
>
> **Robin Cook, former Foreign Secretary and Leader of the House of Commons, UK**

Furthermore, the principle extends beyond politics. Until recently, if you had a complaint against an energy provider, a hospital or a parking meter, say, you could call customer complaints or write to the CEO, but your voice was solitary and singular. Now you can find and join thousands, if not millions, of other people from around the world with similar complaints and put serious pressure on the company. This represents a significant shift of power away from institutions towards individuals. Alone it's difficult to be heard, whereas there's strength in numbers.

Political connectedness Will these developments change the face of politics? We'll have to see, but in theory things should be a great deal more transparent in the future. Indeed, Web 2.0 is perfect for political agitation because it encourages political participation and allows individuals with similar beliefs to find each other then agitate for

Mobile uprisings

The Arab Spring is perhaps a timely reminder of how mobile phones, and in particular social media, can be used to access and disseminate alternative sources of news and information and to mobilize protest and dissent rapidly. In theory, this represents a power struggle between rigid, pyramidal command and control hierarchies (e.g. government and institutions of the state) and fluid, often leaderless, networks of ordinary people. In the case of the Middle East, it has been cast as a battle between authoritarian, anti-democratic despots and freedom-loving citizens, but this needn't always be the case. There is no reason why a democracy could not use the same tools to overthrow a legitimately elected government and replace it with a populist dictator.

change. It also allows politicians to bypass traditional media and conduct conversations with local voters directly. At least that's the theory. In reality, many social media organizations are owned by large corporations, some of whom also own newspapers and television stations and, some might argue, the politicians themselves. Moreover, instead of being ignored by traditional media, individuals with original or unorthodox views may be shouted down by the tyranny of the online majority.

Politics 2.0

Will Web 2.0 and social networks change the face of politics? Quite possibly. For example, Congresspedia (now called Open Congress) was a Wikipedia-style site onto which hundreds, if not thousands, of volunteers posted information about everything from which bills a US politician was sponsoring to where his or her political donations had come from. The result was information and transparency at the click of a mouse. Similarly, Proxy Democracy is a website that empowers small investors to hold large corporations accountable.

We are already connecting with presidents using Twitter and it probably won't be too long before we're voting for prime ministers via Facebook, especially if politicians want to encourage the youth to vote. But connectivity cuts both ways. If we're listening more carefully to them perhaps they're looking more closely at us. There's also the possibility of foreign interests manipulating local politics.

It's been said that the strange sound you sometimes hear when you watch politicians on YouTube is the sound of power draining away from hierarchical institutions such as government and going towards networked individuals. But it's also the sound of power moving in the direction of supranational corporations and, conversely, governments – who are growing stronger due to ubiquitous surveillance.

the condensed idea
Government: control, alt, delete

03 Cyber & drone warfare

Historically, advances in military conflict have, to a large degree, been about the creation of new weapons and this is unlikely to change. Moreover, with the cost of killing rising and the willingness of people to die arguably falling in some regions, the emphasis is shifting more to the use of technology to replace all human contact with the enemy.

Wars used to be about lines and columns of armed men. Then it was about machine guns and artillery and after that tanks and aircraft. But in the future there will be networks of technicians controlling remote devices, some of which will be semi-autonomous. In other words, we are partially moving away from a world of large-scale military hardware and large physical targets to one where stealth attacks and cyber-warfare will be used to destroy specific individuals and elements of urban infrastructure. The aim of such attacks will not be wholesale physical destruction, but short-term disruption and paralysis that will eat away at the hearts and minds of politicians and the public. One of the new vulnerabilities of our digital age is our reliance on technology in general and networks in particular.

Future war We will hear more about cyber-warfare, in particular, because everything from aircraft control systems to power grids, financial markets, telecommunications infrastructure, water pipes and government computer networks are now generally run by computers and are therefore vulnerable to attack. As a survivor of World War Two remarked: 'You don't need a nuclear bomb to get a country to surrender nowadays; you just need to cut the power off for a week.'

timeline

1400–1600	1884	1914	1945	2011
Development of handheld weapons including longbows	First fully automatic submachine gun	Deployment of the first tank	Use of the first atomic bomb	US drone kills Anwar al-Awlaki in Yemen

Terminators: Rise of the machines

Robotic weapons that already exist, or are under development, include:

- **The Throwbot** (a two-wheeled vehicle that can be thrown by hand into a room to search for enemy soldiers using video).

- **LS3** (a four-legged robot that can carry a soldier or up to 180kg/28 stones of equipment for up to 32km/20 miles).

- **The Packbot** (a remote-controlled vehicle primarily used for bomb disposal).

- **Aries** (a small remote-controlled submarine).

- **SMSS** (an unmanned ground vehicle).

- **Maars** (an unmanned, fully armed ground vehicle about the size of a lawn mower).

- **Global Hawk** (an unmanned survey drone).

- **MQ-9 Reaper** (another small unmanned aircraft).

These last two are especially interesting because drones or UAVs potentially represent an interesting blend of human and machine intelligence that's relatively silent, cheap and deadly.

Tactics such as these suit informal terrorist groups and are an example of what's known as asymmetric warfare, where the formal power on one side differs significantly from that of the other. Cyber-war, a form of asymmetric war in many cases, is not limited to the military either. As the cost of winning and losing in business escalates, so too does the temptation to use cyberspace to steal commercial secrets and intellectual property. Moreover, with everyday life moving towards 'the cloud', whereby information is stored remotely and accessed on an on-demand basis, the implications of digital disruption and electronic insecurity (whether government-sponsored or inflicted by politicized geeks, information vigilantes or 'hacktivists') are enormous. Remember too that China has more Internet users than the USA and therefore has a larger hacker population. This means lots of potential cyber-crime and tightly

❝Either war is obsolete or men are.❞

Buckminster Fuller,
author, inventor
and futurist

2020	2021	2023	2025
A third of all US military vehicles are unmanned	A quarter of US army made up of robots	Manned fighter aircraft decommissioned	SWAT teams use insect-like UAVs in civil airspace

> **❝I know not with what weapons World War III will be fought, but World War IV will be fought with sticks and stones.❞**
>
> **Albert Einstein, theoretical physicist**

coordinated electronic spying, some of which is undoubtedly directed at US military installations and defence engineering.

Battlefield robots are another example of semi-autonomous warfare, and more than 50 governments across the globe are actively seeking to develop robotic killing machines. This is partly because the 'value' of human life is increasing due to public opinion, legal redress and the need to win elections, which means that governments will be less willing to risk individual injury and death. Opponents argue that automation will reduce the cost and the emotional investment of warfare, with the result that wars will become more frequent. There is also the issue of mistaken identity – teaching machines to distinguish between military and civilian targets, especially when final decisions about whether to open fire become automated, is especially difficult. On the opposing side, proponents of robotic weapons argue that intelligent fighting machines will pay more attention to battlefield rules and are less likely to engage in acts of anger or malice. They don't panic either.

It all sounds like science fiction, but in fact the development of robotic fighting machines has hardly begun. One machine already created by the US army is a wandering veggie-eating robot. The robot – known as EATR (Energetically Autonomous Tactical Robot) – is able to collect raw biomass such as leaves, wood and grass and convert these into fuel for its steam-powered engine. The robot uses smart software to tell what's edible and what's not and uses a laser-guided robotic arm to grab the biomass and put it in a hopper that connects with an internal combustion engine, which in turn powers an onboard battery. Why do this? The answer is partly that wars depend on energy (soldiers increasingly rely on battery-powered devices) and partly that wars are often fought in remote regions where supply chains can be easily disrupted.

Friend or foe? When it comes to drones, or UAVs (unmanned aerial vehicles), these are principally surveillance tools not weapons at present. Payloads are generally small and they're vulnerable to ground defence because of their slow speed. But give it a few decades and things will change. For example, how about networked drones small enough and responsive enough to enter a house through an open window and transmit information as they travel from room to room? Or perhaps they could be used to monitor traffic, observe forest fires, count livestock, chase criminals and so on. Perhaps we'll see robotic insects with a 3cm (1in) wingspan that could collect information more effectively than a satellite and deliver a tiny biological or chemical payload?

But what happens when the USA loses its lead in drone technology and nations start attacking each other pre-emptively or when terrorist groups use them against civilian targets? Indeed, how about mixing everything up to create a future military, which includes the use of screen-based weapons, remote-controlled aerial drones and joystick-controlled robots? Put another way, what happens when Walt Disney and Hollywood team up to fight the Taliban using 3D glasses, haptic gloves that simulate the sensation of touch and 'scent collars' that create microbursts of cordite?

Will this really happen? Quite possibly. And the reason is a mixture of cost savings and the desire to preserve human life. However, it's not difficult to imagine that the unintended consequences of such developments include a disconnection from reality, real-life risks and understanding, not only on the part of soldiers, but politicians too.

Watching but not necessarily doing

The year is 2022. The US Army has just launched *Call to Arms V*. Within weeks it becomes the most downloaded game of all time, earning $700 million in sales on day one, a figure that easily beats the movie *Avatar 6*, which was launched in the same week and pulls in a paltry $270 million worth of downloads on its first day. *Call to Arms V* has been developed by the US government as a recruiting tool aimed at increasing the number of young soldiers in the US armed forces. However, much as the game appeals to the critical 16–24 age segment, it ultimately fails to pull in very many real recruits, most of whom would rather stay home and play war games on computers.

the condensed idea
War is automated
and moves online

04 Water wars

Is H_2O the new CO_2? Fresh water has always been vital, more important in the short term than either food or energy, and conflicts have been fought over access to water for centuries. Population increases, urbanization, agriculture and industrialization will all increase demand for water in the future, but climate change, pollution and mismanagement all mean that supplies may soon start to evaporate.

The issue, of course, is not fresh water per se, but where it's found and what we choose to do with it. Presently, around a billion people do not have access to safe water and it's estimated that in 20 years half of the world's population will be living in water-stressed regions. Most rainfall runs straight back to the oceans and as much as 70–80 per cent of piped water is lost through leaky pipes and out-of-date technology. We also waste vast amounts of water. We drink, on average, 2–3 litres (4–6 pints) of water per day, but we typically use around 3,000 litres (over 6,000 pints) each in total. Moreover, as the world's population increases and people become richer, their diets change towards water-intensive foods such as meat and, ironically perhaps, fish. According to the International Water Management Institute, a research body, global water demand is expected to grow by 25 per cent by 2030. China, for example, is now home to 20 per cent of the world's population, but has access to only 5 per cent of the world's fresh water supply. Contamination is another issue – around 90 per cent of rivers near urban areas in China are seriously polluted according to a World Bank study. Hence, while the price of food and oil grab the headlines, perhaps we should be worrying more about water.

Over the longer term we will probably have to pay more for fresh water and there will be further water restrictions due to a mixture of soaring

timeline

2003	2008	2010	2011
Washing cars with water banned in Sydney, Australia	70 per cent of major Chinese cities water-stressed	India suspects China of water theft after it builds new dam	Welsh organic water for sale in Los Angeles

demand, climate change and regulation. We will pay for water according to the amount we use, precisely what we use it for, exactly when we use it and water quality. Unmetered water will increasingly be a thing of the past. Water recycling (purifying waste water) will soar and water infrastructure will be upgraded using the latest technology, especially to prevent leakage. Some countries will start to import water, possibly even transporting icebergs, much as they currently import oil, and some water-poor countries may start trading commodities, such as oil, for clean water.

Expect to see water theft emerging as a major problem, with legal action being initiated by one country, or region, against another for water shortages created by cloud seeding – the artificial, or at least premature, creation of rain from water-laden clouds via the sprinkling of, typically, dry ice or silver iodine into clouds – or geo-engineering projects. Also expect to see a shift in agriculture towards less thirsty crops. Indeed, social pressure may even make the eating of certain types of foodstuffs socially

> **'Water is the oil of the 21st Century.'**
> **Andrew Liveris, CEO, The Dow Chemical Company**

The cost of convenience

In the 1970s, the American water industry was based around sales of big bottles for home and office, until Perrier stepped in. Their plan was to market water as a drink, just like Coke or alcohol. First they linked bottled water to exclusivity, then they connected Perrier to health, and finally associated the brand with celebrity. Now Americans drink more bottled water than milk, coffee or beer and in many instances it costs more per litre than petrol. Will this situation continue in the future or will bottled water be banned on the basis that it's a needless extravagance that wastes water and creates unwanted emissions?

2021	2032	2038	2050
Sana'a in Yemen becomes first major city to run out of water	Las Vegas runs out of water	Water labelling of all consumer products	Global pricing for a barrel of water (150 litres)

> **❝The Romans realized, as have every civilized people since, that living in cities is impossible if the water supply is not reliably clean and fresh.❞**
>
> **Frank Chapelle,** author of *Wellsprings* and *Ground-water Microbiology and Geochemistry*

unacceptable in the future – lettuce, for example, squanders what is, after all, the most precious resource on Earth.

There's also the issue of conflict created by too much water. If climate change impacts on the world in the way that some suspect, flooding in low-lying coastal areas may trigger unregulated mass population movements. Combined with shortages of food and energy, this may cause internal unrest and ultimately state collapse, especially in developing countries.

Cause of conflict But water isn't just a problem on the land. Oceans can also become catalysts for conflict between nations, especially those with a hunger for fish, as anyone old enough to remember the Icelandic Cod wars will recall. And let's not forget that access to the sea floor brings with it vast riches in the form of oil, coal and perhaps rare minerals. Water has been a catalyst for conflict in the past – Darfur in Sudan being perhaps the most recent example – and there is little reason to believe that water won't create conflict in the future. The Indus Waters Treaty, for instance, whereby India and Pakistan have agreed to share water from the River Indus fairly, could lead to significant tensions between India and Pakistan if water availability declines or water prices increase.

Even if water isn't the primary cause of local warfare it can still reshape geopolitics. For instance, did you know that around 90 per cent of the world's opium poppies are located in Afghanistan and that 90 per cent of these plants reside in Helmand province? Perhaps you did, but did you also realize that it was the destruction of the region's canal system during the 1980s Afghanistan war and the drought that followed during the 1990s that is largely responsible for farmers in the area switching from fruit growing to poppy production?

Water matters To sum up: in the future, water could well prove to be a bigger threat to national security and economic well-being than oil and terrorism combined, and we will see some radical attempts to change attitudes and behaviour surrounding the use of water at both the societal and the household level.

Too much or not enough?

When Pakistan flooded recently, it was hard to believe the country had a critical shortage of fresh water. This is not only devastating for its citizens, but was a direct threat to American security because a lack of water can fuel conflict. The Middle East and North Africa contain the 16 most water-troubled states in the world, all using more water than they receive (Libya uses 700 times more). As populations increase, aquifers can run dry and oil for desalination plants can run out, creating a triple crisis in water, food and energy, any one of which can trigger trouble. These three basic human needs will always be inextricably linked. While the global population increased by a third in the 20th century, demand for water increased six-fold and this trend is likely to continue.

Examples may include consumer and industrial products indicating on a label (or, more likely, on a product's virtual duplicate) how much water was used in its manufacture. 'Virtual water' (sometimes known as embedded water) is an idea developed by Tony Allan of King's College London and is intended to convey to anyone who's interested the volume of water 'absorbed' by a product or service during its creation and delivery. Virtual water can be applied to anything from a cotton t-shirt or a bottle of cola to a hamburger or a car and the politics surrounding all this is likely to be a strong feature of the future.

the condensed idea
The world runs
out of water

05 Wane of the West

In 2001 Goldman Sachs, a global investment bank, listed Brazil, Russia, India and China as the four (BRIC) countries that would dominate the global economy by 2041. China has already replaced Japan as the world's second-largest economy and may overtake the United States as early as 2027.

Jim O'Neill, Chief Economist of Goldman Sachs, coined the acronym 'BRICs' in a briefing paper issued in London on November 30, 2001. The briefing (*Building Better Economic BRICs*) described how Brazil, Russia, India and China, all chosen on the basis of population, economic development and attitudes towards globalization, were reshaping the world in terms of economic power. The briefing note also boldly predicted that by 2041 (then revised to 2039) these nations would eclipse the six largest Western nations with regard to economic output. In other words, Russia, Brazil, India and China would soon reshape the world, not only in terms of money, but also in terms of influence and ideas.

Critics immediately dismissed the BRIC concept as self-interested spin, especially because their figures were based upon a linear extrapolation way out to 2050 and because China already had by far the strongest economy, certainly in terms of growth. Some critics even tried to respond with acronyms of their own. As a result we saw BRIMC (adding Mexico), CHIME (China, India, Middle East) and even the CEMENT bloc (Countries Excluded from the Emerging New Terminology). Even Goldman Sachs had another go, coining the new acronym N11 to describe the Next Eleven economic powerhouses (Bangladesh, Egypt, Indonesia,

timeline

2011	2012	2014	2016
China becomes world's second-largest economy	90 per cent of scientists and engineers with PhDs live in Asia	China surpasses USA in scientific research	Brazil is world's fourth-largest economy

Iran, South Korea, Mexico, Nigeria, Pakistan, Philippines, Turkey and Vietnam).

However, despite the cynicism, nobody to date has managed to shoot the BRIC tag down. In fact, following the global recession that started in 2007/8, the concept seems stronger than ever. Asian and southern economic power is still rising and, with the arguable exception of Russia, all of the BRIC nations have emerged from the Global Financial Crisis (GFC) stronger economically than their Western counterparts, which are suffering varying degrees of decline. Goldman now predicts that China will eclipse the USA economically by 2027 and that the BRIC bloc will overtake the six leading Western nations by 2031 – ten years sooner than originally predicted.

> **'Here lies a sleeping giant, let him sleep, for when he wakes up, he will shock the world.'**
>
> **Napoleon,** speaking about China in 1803

Will the wall fall?

Could the BRIC wall collapse? China's future growth is certainly at a crossroads. It has enjoyed double-digit growth for almost a decade, but there is a school of opinion that says this cannot continue hand in glove with the country's resolutely communist regime. Furthermore, economic growth in China has so far presumed state investment in huge infrastructure projects underpinned by cheap labour, which is rapidly running out. As for Russia, it's a similar story. In India's case the country is straining due to 60 years of under-investment in critical infrastructure and there is the issue of ponderous bureaucracy and corruption. Brazil is looking good, but it's not growing as fast as many people predicted. All of which may leave the USA, together with a few N11 wildcards, such as South Korea, Turkey, Vietnam and Iran, in strong positions in the future.

2018	2019	2025	2039
China opens 60 new airports in five years	Reverse immigration to Asia threatens US economy	China becomes the world's largest economy	Chinese yuan becomes world's base currency

The rise of the middle classes So where do things stand currently? Globalization is continuing and parts of Asia, Africa and South America are becoming more affluent and economically important. This doesn't necessarily imply a military threat, but culturally and economically the West is set for relative decline and tensions will rise.

This applies not only to Western-inspired global institutions, but also to Western belief systems and brands. Moreover, the BRIC concept isn't a purely intellectual exercise. For example, since China has now become the world's leading car market, this has implications for demand for Brazilian copper. Thus asset prices can be adjusted. Goldman's estimate that by 2030 there will be 2 billion new middle-class consumers living on the planet boosts demand for other resources, commodities and products ranging from oil, gas, coal, potash and water to lithium, copper, cardboard and even cheese.

Test of strength So, will the BRICs keep growing or could some cracks start to appear in the bloc? The most likely outcome is exactly what Goldman says it is – that the BRIC nations will largely dominate the world economy. However, it could also turn out that the bloc, like Europe, is a disparate group and it's quite likely that one or more of the nations could fall over financially or become isolationist, turning inwards.

China, arguably, has a property bubble in the making, its financial system is suspect (shades of the Japanese banking system prior to their 'lost decade'), water is an issue, they are running out of low-cost rural migrants and the imbalance of young males in China's population could cause trouble if economic growth slows and unemployment starts to rise. Meanwhile, Russia is a tinderbox politically and Brazil's prospects seem to rise and fall all the time depending upon the latest economic numbers and the whims of newspaper and magazine editors. This leaves India, where infrastructure is being pushed to its physical limits and where corruption is endemic. Even Japan, which is outside the group, is a case study in historical ebb and flow, illustrating how economic might doesn't always translate into global muscle.

> **Consider the past and you shall know the future.**
> Chinese proverb

Two banks, two scenarios

Two big banks, Citigroup and HSBC, have developed two different visions of what the world could look like in the future. According to Citigroup, the West is finished. By 2050, for instance, Indonesia's GDP will eclipse that of Germany, France, Italy and the UK combined, and together the economies of China and India will be 400 per cent larger than the USA. Meanwhile, the fastest-growing region will be Africa (growing at 7.5 per cent per year over the next 20 years). HSBC, in contrast, believes that the West is about to enter a period of unparalleled prosperity. Yes, China does overtake the USA in economic terms, but only just and the world ends up being ruled by a G2 of China and America – not China and India. The reason for this is the US fertility rate, which means that Americans end up 300 per cent richer than the Chinese in 2050 and this gives rise to a totally different geopolitical picture.

This leaves the USA, which is probably far more resilient than most people realize, thanks to a mix of favourable demographics (a high fertility rate plus a 'can do' attitude towards immigration) and cultural factors that include the American Dream. Even so, things could get nasty. If the global economy moves in the way that some people predict, what we'll see is a huge structural shift whereby the East becomes vastly wealthier than the West. In Europe, for instance, this could mean rising expectations meeting declining opportunities and incomes. This could, in turn, lead to anger and resentment, which will create a fertile environment for extremist politicians offering xenophobic and protectionist solutions.

the condensed idea
Wealth and influence move eastwards

06 Resource depletion

We are entering a period where demand for natural resources, especially oil, is rising rapidly due to economic development and population growth, while known finite reserves are simultaneously declining. According to the International Energy Agency, we use 85 million barrels of oil every day – forecast to be 105 million barrels per day by 2030 – and they predict that 'output of conventional oil will peak in 2020 if oil demand grows on a business-as-usual basis'.

Do oil producers have the rest of the world over a barrel? Yes and no. Oil is running out, alongside other key resources, but the amount that's left is probably much more than we think and largely depends on what price people are willing to pay for it.

With oil, in particular, technology will rapidly develop alongside demand, as it has done historically. This means that deeper deposits will be accessed alongside new reserves. Furthermore, 'peak oil' generally refers to conventional oil, but there are huge reserves of unconventional oils such as tar sands, ultra-heavy oils, oil shales and bituminous schist. Over the next few decades we'll have problems matching rising demand to supply, but the main issues will be price volatility, transport and refining capacity – not a lack of oil. And let's not forget that higher prices are an incentive for people to use resources more wisely and to develop highly cost-efficient alternatives. Nevertheless, in 2030, we will still rely on oil for around 29 per cent of our energy needs and the world is still likely to get at least 75 per cent of its energy from oil, coal and gas.

timeline

1999	2007	2008	2011
Oil costs $10 a barrel	Oil costs $147 a barrel	Economic crash causes collapse of oil price	Price of copper results in widespread metal theft from railways

Countering the crisis Countries such as the USA and Canada have vast reserves of shale gas and there's lots of coal too – if only we could figure out a way to make it cleaner. According to some pessimistic commentators (notably Richard Heinberg), declining reserves of oil will lead to 'abrupt and revolutionary' change, which possibly includes a 1930s-style depression. And that's before we factor in climate change. This is obviously why there is so much interest in alternative energy. But there are problems here too. Most alternative energy technologies, with the possible exception of solar, do not scale up to anything like the degree that's required, and many are currently economically viable only due to government subsidies. Nevertheless, it has been estimated that solar energy could still provide 15 per cent of Europe's energy needs by 2050 and there are plans to build vast solar farms in North Africa for this purpose. Wind, wave and geothermal solutions look much less promising (see Chapter 7).

> **❝Oil depletion and climate change will create an entirely new context in which political struggles will be played out.❞**
>
> **Richard Heinberg,** author

global warning

What will happen with climate change? The answer is that we don't know – not in terms of precise effects and definitely not in terms of the human reaction to these effects. We do not know how fast sea levels will rise, how climate change will impact on specific regions, how great any cooling effects will be, how much hotter things will get or how far greenhouse gas levels will rise. Most of all, we do not know whether the world, or which parts of it, will ignore climate change and focus instead on the pursuit of fossil fuels and narrow short-term self-interest. Two things that do seem likely: we will do too little too late and something will happen that nobody is currently expecting.

2017	**2026**	**2028**	**2038**
Drilling for oil in the Arctic commences	Oil costs $200 a barrel	Denmark becomes world's first oil-free country	Saudi Arabia becomes a net importer of oil

> **The energy future we are facing today, based on projections of current trends, is dirty, insecure and expensive.**
>
> **Claude Mandil,**
> **International Energy Agency**

What about nuclear fission? Conventional nuclear energy will be a firm feature of the future, but it needs uranium and that's ultimately a finite resource too. But even here perhaps we're being overly pessimistic. The Nuclear Energy Agency says that uranium resources stand at around 5.5 million metric tons, with an extra 10.5 million metric tons still undiscovered. That's probably enough uranium for the next 200 years at today's consumption levels. Additional exploration techniques and extraction technologies will almost certainly increase these figures over time. Meanwhile, the uranium needs of reactors could fall by up to 30 per cent, while extracting plutonium and uranium from spent uranium to make new fuel may mean that requirements reduce by another 30 per cent.

As for fusion power, that's a serious possibility, but not before 2050 at the earliest. Fusion power is essentially the process of artificially creating here on Earth what the Sun does naturally out in space. If we could master this, the prize would be low-cost energy that could fuel human inventiveness for centuries to come. We shouldn't forget the promise of artificial photosynthesis either – essentially, the idea of making energy out of nothing more than sunlight, water and carbon dioxide.

Small steps So, in the meantime what can we do? The short answer is panic, because things are going to get rather bumpy over the next few decades, not just in relation to fossil fuels, but with other key resources such as water and foodstuffs too. As for climate change, this is not looking good either, especially over the longer term.

Of course, implicit in this discussion is the idea that we need a high-technology solution. Yet simply turning things off, or not using devices or appliances at certain times of day, could make an enormous difference. According to the US Department of Energy, global electricity demand will rise by 77 per cent by 2030. Yet simply designing fuel-efficient devices, factories and cars (relatively simple technology) could

Resource nationalism

Ten of the largest oil companies in the world are 'nationals' – state-controlled oil companies. Moreover, many of the owners of the world's largest remaining oil fields are moving to the far left politically and could potentially nationalize all energy and resource production within their borders. Venezuela is frequently quoted as a future trouble spot as it contains some of the world's largest remaining reserves, but Nigeria (which has the eighth-largest oil reserves on Earth), Libya, Bolivia, Peru, Ecuador, Angola and Sudan could also potentially shut out foreign oil and resource companies from their soil. We are already witnessing the rush of countries such as China into regions including Africa, and many of these buyers are willing to deal with these regimes on a 'no questions asked' basis. So what are some of the potential future scenarios for oil politics? One possibility is that a US attack on Iran will result in an Iranian blockage of oil moving through the Strait of Hormuz (20 per cent of the world's traded oil passes through this chokepoint, so this could be devastating, although unlikely to succeed over a longer period). A more plausible development would be a radicalized Nigeria. Rebels could halt oil production in the southern delta region and this could lead to a Muslim general seizing power in the north, which in turn could result in US military intervention.

reduce demand by 20–33 per cent. But changing how we use energy is not that straightforward: our infrastructure is largely designed for oil, not alternatives such as shale gas. The argument that we need a radical technology revolution to save the planet, however, is not necessarily true.

the condensed idea
Energy demand exceeds supply

07 Beyond fossil fuels

The average Californian uses around 40 per cent less electricity than the average American. Per capita, energy use in California has remained flat in recent years, while in the rest of the USA it has soared by 50 per cent. Why? Part of the reason is climate. But in sunny California, the 1973 oil crisis also sparked a change in attitudes and an interest in technologies that might one day save the planet.

Over the next couple of decades, short-term economic self-interest is likely to underwrite the world's addiction to fossil fuels. This means that oil-, coal- and gas-exporting states will rise in political influence and the nuclear issue will not go away. But markets respond to demand, and for this reason alone the distant future is looking brighter. Moreover, the universe is full of energy. Most of our own planet is bathed in solar energy every single day, so what we are really facing is not an energy crisis so much as a crisis of human imagination and ingenuity.

The search for energy New energy technologies on the horizon include integrated photovoltaics, whereby semiconductors are designed to create an electric current due to exposure to light. Photovoltaic panels could be embedded within the walls, roofs or even windows of large buildings, thereby transforming many structures into net exporters of energy (producing more energy than they use).

Other energy sources being developed include geothermal (heat from deep inside the Earth) and various forms of kinetic energy, including wind

timeline

1973	2020	2025
First oil crisis	Launch of North African solar grid	Oil, coal and gas still responsible for 70 per cent of energy supply

(windmills on the ground, but also giant kites in the air tethered to the ground or ships), and wave energy. There's also energy generated from the impact of human legs on urban pavements, or the turning of wheels initially powered by other energy sources. Then there are some innovative energy-conservation technologies, such as lunar-dimming streetlights that give out less light when the Moon is bright.

Could biofuels be the answer? Not in their current form. Using crops to make fuel soaks up carbon while they're growing, but they also displace existing established vegetation, which often grows more reliably. Growing fuel crops on unused industrial land is fine, but we often cut down virgin forest to plant fuel crops. Some studies suggest that biofuels also push up food prices, although others contest this.

> **'In time, manufacturing will to a great extent follow the sun.'**
>
> **C.G. Abbot (1928), discussing the prospect of deserts being turned into industrial zones due to the development of solar energy**

californification

According to some observers, California is a failed state. It is dysfunctional. Its budget is bust. Its schools are failing. It has gridlocked traffic, failing infrastructure and overcrowded prisons. It's short of water too. All of this is true. But looking at things differently, California is a model for the future, not only for America, but also for the global economy. Economically, demographically, culturally and technologically, California is on the cutting edge. California is the most globalized state in the USA – and the greenest. It is the world's seventh-largest economy, with 38 million residents. It's also an incubator of new ideas – especially ideas relating to clean energy and transport, many of which are being funded by industry 'outsiders' with backgrounds in high-tech areas.

2030	**2045**	**2050**
Global energy demand up by 50 per cent over 2008 levels	Clean energy islands built off the coast of China	First commercial thorium reactor

> **Every time you look up at the sky,
> every one of those points of light is
> a reminder that fusion power is extractable
> from hydrogen and other light elements.**
>
> **Carl Sagan**, astronomer, astrophysicist and cosmologist

One way of solving these problems is to develop new forms of genetically engineered biofuels (algae that produce basic hydrocarbons including octane, for example), but so far these ideas mostly exist in research laboratories rather than inside your petrol tank. Nevertheless, expect to see next-generation biofuel 'factories' both in marine environments and on land.

Changing attitude Some of these technologies won't make much of a difference on their own. But they don't need to. If we can change how, when and where we consume energy, ideas such as these will all add up to a serious solution, especially when used in conjunction with smart energy efficiency and conservation measures.

There's also the idea that electricity (and other precious resources such as water), should be priced according to end use. For example, electrically powered carving knives, pencil sharpeners and garden leaf blowers are an extravagance and could be replaced with human-powered alternatives, so why not price or tax them accordingly? Add to this hyper-local energy networks (see Chapter 12) and the winds of change may soon start to blow in the right direction.

In the distant energy future, we shouldn't discount big ideas such as fusion reactors, thorium reactors or energy harvested from space via giant solar panels, which is beamed back to vast collecting stations back on Earth using gigantic space-to-Earth microwaves or lasers (see Chapter 37).

However, while most eyes are on a technological prize, we shouldn't ignore some very old, non-emerging technologies. It is generally assumed that new is always more powerful and more useful than old, but this isn't always the case. Ford's 2007 car fleet, for instance, averaged 18.7mpg.

Yet in 1908, the Model T Ford could reach 25mpg. Well-designed small cars with highly efficient petrol engines can make a huge difference, especially when new lightweight batteries can store some of the kinetic energy they produce in motion and sell this back to a local electricity network. Maybe this is also a way to store and transfer power on a larger scale, thereby making national electricity grids more responsive to surges in demand. And while we're at it, why not replace national grids with micro-networks owned and operated by small energy entrepreneurs?

Synthetic biology

The idea that science can create artificial life is disturbing, so we give it less threatening names such as 'synthetic biology' or the more edgy, 'synbio'. Yet advances in this field are progressing rapidly and some of the practical uses of this technology could be exciting and life-enhancing – reducing climate change or restoring an extinct species. A team led by Dr Craig Venter has replicated the genome of *Mycoplasma genitalium*. His stated aims are to discover the 'minimal genome', the one needed for survival and reproduction, and to combine genomics with technology, for example, using modified bacteria to make fuels.

Let's not forget about some other ideas from the past either, such as sailing ships, horse-drawn barges or bicycles. Even railways, done right, could have an enormous impact. And we could always walk a bit more, put on a jumper when it's cold and dry our wet clothes on a washing line outside rather than inside in a tumble dryer. Finally, and most optimistically perhaps, let's not forget about the energy potential of genetic engineering, especially the use of synthetic biology to produce new micro-organisms that do things that nature historically hasn't – for instance, secrete bio-diesel.

the condensed idea
Don't panic, we're inventive

08 Precision agriculture

Global population growth (more precisely, global income growth) will challenge the ability of agriculture to deliver maximum productivity in the future, especially if climate change negatively affects agricultural yields. Until quite recently farmers used experience mixed with trial-and-error to produce crops, but things are changing down on the farm.

'Precision agriculture' is a term used to describe the use of hyper-specific GPS (global positioning systems) and digital mapping to control precisely the application of seeds, pesticides and water to crops and, on occasion, to manage livestock. For example, precise satellite imagery of fields enables farmers to vary the delivery of chemicals down to areas as small as 2.5cm (1in) – or a single plant. This means minimum waste and pesticide residue runoff into adjacent habitats, and maximum profitability. Such use of GPS is made even more accurate by the use of real-time kinematics – essentially the use of fixed GPS receivers with their own longitude and latitude to deliver additional information about the local terrain and bolster satellite accuracy.

In some instances, the system is so precise that seeds can be planted at exactly the same spot that fertilizer granules were spread months earlier. So what's the future of technology-aided farming? In the UK, 13 per cent of farmers are now using auto-steering on farm machinery and we will soon see the development of automated, driverless vehicles that work, alone, out in the fields. From there it's not much of a leap to semi-intelligent harvester robots or robots that can go off by themselves to look for weeds or sick animals. The idea of self-driving cars has been a staple of science

timeline

1755	1845	1917	1942
Marie Antoinette alleged to have said, 'Let them eat cake'	Start of Irish potato famine	Sugar rationing in UK	Coffee rationing in USA

6In the long term, economic sustainability depends on ecological sustainability.9
Pew Oceans Report, 2003

fiction for many decades, but in reality we are likely to see self-driving farm machinery and military vehicles far sooner than we will see serious numbers of automated vehicles on public roads, largely because many of the safety and legal concerns that apply to road use do not apply quite so much on private farmland or battlefields.

If you find all this a little fanciful, consider for a moment that there is already a system in use in parts of the UK whereby video feeds are used to monitor animals automatically, working out when they're ready to be slaughtered. The technology maps animal outlines, then uses algorithms to work out weight, feed requirements and likely market days. Why bother? Because of cost savings and profit maximization.

Vertical farming

What if 'eating locally' meant buying food from a local supermarket that had a 30-storey farm above it? What if the Hanging Gardens of Babylon became the hanging vegetable gardens of Brooklyn? Dickson Despommier, a professor at Columbia University, had the idea of vertical city farms back in 1999 and the concept seems to have captured the imagination of numerous architects around the world. By 2050, 80 per cent of the world's population will live in cities. Given the need for land and the pressure to reduce transportation, high-rise farms will perhaps be built in the middle of cities such as London and New York.

1974	1996	2011	2032
Hybrid rice in China	GMO foods in Europe	Cost of meat leads to surge in meat theft in UK supermarkets	Open-ocean aquaculture provides 80 per cent of the world's seafood

3 meals from a riot

In August 2010, food prices increased by 5 per cent globally. Prices were still 30 per cent lower than they had been in 2008, but this didn't prevent trouble in some places. In Mozambique, bread prices rose by 30 per cent and ten people died as a result of subsequent food riots. So what's next? Even with depressed growth in advanced economies, another surge in food prices is on the horizon and this could, once again, spell trouble. Food has been cheap for a long time, but this situation will change unless we can invent new ways of creating food. For example, as meat becomes more expensive, we will see a shift towards less expensive types of meat and even towards proteins that are not usually considered edible by most people – for example, insects.

Fishing without fishermen But applying cutting-edge science and technology to the food chain won't be limited to the land. Out at sea similar techniques will be applied to farm fish in the open ocean. The idea here is to build vast motorized – or possibly sail-powered – cages, fill them with laboratory-bred baby fish and float them out to sea. Food can either come from the open ocean or be scattered into the cages from supply vessels, which know exactly where the cages are thanks, once again, to GPS. Cameras linked to algorithms can work out the size and number of fish that each cage contains, then find out where your end customer is. You can then sail the cage to its final destination, where it's picked up by a tug and towed into port. No airfreight, costly long-distance shipping or refrigeration necessary. 'Open-ocean aquaculture' is set to revolutionize how fish are farmed and harvested.

Of course, you might be wondering why on earth we need such things and the answer is necessity. As incomes grow in regions such as Asia and Africa attitudes and behaviours towards food tend to change.

Out goes a subsistence diet of local fruit and vegetables and in comes a taste for meat, and especially fish if you're concerned about health issues (e.g. Chinese consumption of fish increased from 11.5kg/25lb per person in 1990 to a whopping 25.6kg/56lb per person in 2006). That's why 28 per cent of fish stocks are already overfished or close to extinction, so something has to be done quickly. In Thai waters, for example, overall fish density fell by 86 per cent from 1961–1991. In the not too distant future, we will see large-scale farming of fish in deserts. It takes just 10 litres (21 pints) of water to grow 1kg (2lb) of fish in a desert compared to 750 litres (1,500 pints) of water to grow a kilo of wheat.

Casting the net wider So watch out for a number of fascinating developments coming out of regions blessed with lots of unused, or under-utilized, semi-arid land and that also have lots of sunshine (to create power) and access to at least some water. Parts of the Middle East spring to mind as a perfect location for 'agricultural property development', but so too do parts of the USA, Australia and Latin America.

It's forecast that food production globally will have to increase by 50 per cent by 2030 and to double by the year 2050 to feed the planet's rapidly growing population. If this is true, it presents something of a challenge, but we have been here before to some extent. Back in the late 1700s and early 1800s Thomas Malthus predicted that the world would run into severe trouble because agricultural production would not be able to keep pace with population growth. He was absolutely right about population growth, but totally wrong about agricultural productivity and the ways in which free-market mechanisms respond to demand. Once again we are on the cusp of serious trouble in terms of resources, especially food, but once again one suspects that human imagination will save the day, especially over the longer term. *Qui vivra, verra* ('Who lives will see' – in other words, time will tell).

> **The belly rules the mind.**
> **Spanish proverb**

the condensed idea
Agriculture will get smarter

09 Population change

From 1900 to 2000 the human population nearly quadrupled from 1.6 billion to 6.1 billion. In 2011 it reached 7 billion and, according to one UN scenario, will hit 8 billion in 2025, 9 billion in 2043 and 10 billion in 2083. Or perhaps not. The final number depends on the fertility rate plus or minus wars, pandemics, accidents and a few other factors.

Why is the world's population growing? The answer is not what you might think. The reason for the explosion is not that people have been reproducing like rabbits, but that people have stopped dropping dead like flies. In 1900, the average global life expectancy was 30 years. By 2000 it was 65. But while increasing health was a hallmark of the 20th century, declining fertility could be a defining feature of the 21st.

Birth rate variations According to the UN Population Division and the US Census Bureau, the average number of births per woman has fallen from 4.9 in the early 1960s to 2.5 nowadays. Furthermore, around 50 per cent of the world's population live in regions where the figure is now below the replacement level (i.e. 2.1 births per woman) and almost all developed nations are experiencing sub-replacement fertility. You might think that developing nations would make up the shortfall (especially since 80 per cent of the world's people now reside in such nations), but you'd be wrong. Declining fertility is a major problem in many developing regions too. If economic growth returns to pre-recession levels, we could soon see catastrophic global manpower shortages within a few decades.

timeline

10,000 BC	1810	1930	1950	1970	1980
World population 1 million	World population 1 billion	2 billion	2.4 billion	3.7 billion	4.4 billion

Who and how many?

One fascinating by-product of the trend towards smaller families is that if a generation has fewer offspring, its genetic legacy is reduced. This may mean that the beliefs that a generation adhered to will weaken over time. In the USA it has been shown that people who decide to have children tend to be more conservative than people that don't, so conservative values may strengthen. For example, in 2004, states that voted for the conservative George W. Bush had fertility rates that were 12 per cent higher on average than states that voted for the more secular, individualistic and liberal-leaning John Kerry. This may be a particularly American phenomenon, but it is certainly true that to a large degree the future is demographically driven. If you want to look at the longer-term future of the Arab–Israeli conflict, look at which groups are having children and which are not.

Since 1990, increases in population have largely occurred in China and India. But this will change. Over the next 20 years, the largest increases will be in sub-Saharan Africa (around 33 per cent of the total). Other areas that will experience rises include Bangladesh and Pakistan. Together, China, India, Bangladesh and Pakistan will be responsible for almost half of all global increases.

Breaking the data down by age group also reveals some additional surprises. The greatest decline in young manpower will occur in China, for instance. The implications? First, China needs to undergo rapid economic development before a demographic implosion hits the country. Second, if other factors such as technology remain constant, economic growth and material expectations (and consumer spending) will fall considerably below recent norms and this could unleash trouble.

1990	2000	2011	2030	2040	2050	2075
5.1 billion	6.1 billion	7 billion	8 billion	8.8 billion	9.1 billion	9.2 billion

> **The battle to feed all of humanity is over. In the 1970s and 1980s hundreds of millions of people will starve to death in spite of any crash programs embarked upon now.**
>
> Paul Ehrlich, author of *The Population Bomb* (1968)

Economic impacts aside, in China there are 120 boys for every 100 girls and this gender imbalance could create a generation of disturbed young men. Forecasts suggest that by 2030 more than a quarter of young Chinese men in their late 30s will never have married – and will perhaps never do so. Other implications include a shift in innovation clusters towards areas with younger populations (because youth is one of the key drivers of innovation) and rising levels of discontent.

Russia is another country with demographic problems that could derail its economic promise. Since 1992 the number of people dying has outnumbered those being born by a massive 50 per cent. Indeed official figures suggest the country has shrunk by 5 per cent since 1993 and life expectancy is marginally lower than it was in 1961. Why is this occurring? Nobody is quite sure, but poor diet and above all chronic alcoholism have much to do with it. If current trends don't bend, Russia's population will be about the size of Yemen's by the year 2050.

In the north of India, the population is booming due to high fertility rates, but in the south, where most economic development is taking place, fertility is falling rapidly. In a further twist, fertility is highest in poorly educated rural areas and lowest in highly educated urban areas. In total, 25 per cent of India's working-age population has no education whatsoever. In 2030, a sixth of the country's potential workforce could be totally uneducated. As for Japan, the fertility rate is approximately 35 per cent below the necessary replacement level and this has huge implications for productivity and public debt. Western Europe is not quite in this position, but the region is expected to experience population stagnation, with Germany – the region's economic powerhouse – experiencing population decline.

The American model One solution is obviously to import foreign workers via immigration, but this has been problematic for some nations, especially Japan. As for the USA, it is almost unique among OECD (Organisation for Economic Co-operation and Development) nations in having a population that is expected to grow by 20 per cent from

The cost of dying

One of the big issues facing Western countries is the cost of supporting rapidly ageing populations with pensions, especially with declining fertility rates and rising healthcare costs. However, while rising life expectancy and falling fertility rates are real, reactions may be unnecessarily alarmist. People are living longer, but they are also living more healthily. The problem is really the cost of dying, and some evidence suggests this can fall with age. There is also the possibility that new innovations will keep people healthy for longer or reduce the cost of dying. Automation may also produce large economic surpluses to pay for ageing.

2010–2030. Moreover, the USA has a track record of successfully assimilating immigrants. As a result it's likely to see a rise in the size of its working-age population and to witness strong economic growth over the longer term.

Of course, all these estimates could be wildly off the mark. Perhaps another great famine, global pandemic or a world war could kill off billions of people, or maybe people will suddenly start having much larger families for reasons of economic survival or for status. In theory, demographic forecasting is a relatively scientific field, but in reality it can be subject to the vagaries of the future just like anything else.

the condensed idea
Too many people in some places, not enough in others

10 Geo-engineering

The Earth's climate is changing and it's probably our fault. But beyond regulation, taxation and pricing, can much be done, especially on a global scale? Can we agree who's at fault and who or what is in charge of sorting things out? Most importantly, can we get a consensus to unleash the power of science and technology to augment our Earth's natural systems?

Why are we Earthlings so devoted to the idea that evolution has stopped (with us) or that the Earth is something we must protect and preserve? It's highly unlikely that we are the pinnacle of evolutionary development. Either we will die out soon and another form of life will take our place as the dominant species on Earth or we will merge with our machines and one day move on to the far-flung corners of the galaxy and temporarily colonize other planets.

Neither scenario necessarily involves the total destruction of the Earth, which will, in all probability, carry on just fine without us, just as it did before us. The Earth does not need icecaps, rainforests or deserts, or specific sea levels. These elements have always changed with the passage of geological time and it is arrogant and egocentric on one level to assume that the Earth needs us – or needs us to save it. Indeed, it might get along much better without us.

Another assumption is implicit in most contemporary thinking about the Earth and its preservation: we shouldn't change it. But we've been changing the Earth for thousands of years. We've been cutting down forests, building dwellings, creating roads, diverting rivers, growing crops, expanding cities, digging giant holes in the ground to extract resources and

timeline

2019	2021	2025	2027
Nobel Prize awarded for a geo-solution to climate change	World's first large-scale ocean fertilization trial begins	Carbon capture technologies widely adopted	Large areas of Venice, Miami and Dhaka abandoned due to flooding

Keep it simple

Why are we so focused on highly technical and hugely expensive fixes to the Earth's climate problems? Perhaps the reason is a belief that complex systems need complex solutions? Or maybe it's our mindset, which says that if relatively complicated engineering got us into this mess, why shouldn't we use technology to get us out? But what if we went in the opposite direction? What if, instead of building mirrors or curtains in space, or spraying seawater into the air, we simply changed human behaviour? What if we used pricing or taxation to modify everyday life? For example, if the purchase price or use of an electric tumble dryer became oxorbitantly expensive, many people would rapidly switch to a simple clothesline instead.

such like since we've been on the planet. And the only real difference of late is scale. To argue that nature should be left alone is nonsense on one level. As the writer Julian Gough has pointed out: 'Nature was fun while it lasted, but humans own the planet now. We might as well decorate it.'

What does he mean by this? I suspect he is referring to what's known as geo-engineering. This is the use of science, technology and large-scale engineering to modify the Earth's structure and systems to combat climate change, either by removing carbon dioxide from the atmosphere or by managing incoming solar radiation. Nature, in one sense, is just raw materials and we shouldn't worry too much about reshaping things.

> **We are upsetting the atmosphere upon which all life depends.**
> David Suzuki, academic and author

2030
Creation of artificial
forests to scrub carbon
from the air

2040
Development of cloud
whitening above the
world's oceans

2050
The global space
mirror project
abandoned due to cost

Clearing up our own mess After all, if human actions have created a problem, why shouldn't human actions help to solve it? We might, for example, sprinkle billions of mirrors in space or produce space curtains to deflect the Sun's rays. Or we might seed the oceans with iron to encourage the growth of phytoplankton to absorb CO_2, or shoot sulphur into the atmosphere to reflect sunlight.

Other ideas include using the oceans to create clouds – scooping up seawater and spraying it into the air – or pumping nutrient-rich water from the bottom of the oceans to block sunlight, as well as various forms of carbon capture (sequestration). Or perhaps we can create artificial forests to remove CO_2 from our atmosphere, or build a giant chemistry set to deal with ocean acidification or stored heat?

Each of these ideas is incredibly expensive and many would say simplistic or even quite barmy, but then again, that's how most radical ideas appear at first. Some scientists also say that it's already too late to put any of these practices into place. They warn, too, that such ideas are no substitute for making much-needed changes to human attitudes and behaviour, especially where finite resources are concerned.

The carbon credit fiasco

Not so long ago, carbon trading didn't exist. Now we have a whole industry based on the idea that you can precisely count offsets and that firms should be allowed to trade in pollution. One job that didn't exist in the past is an emissions assessor. This is the person who visits a site to determine whether a promised emission reduction or offset package stacks up. In theory, this should be easy; in practice, it's not. For example, the journal *Climate Policy* found that 60 per cent of clean energy or offset projects would have happened without carbon trading. Moreover, 15–20 per cent of carbon credits should not have been issued because the people behind the projects failed to produce proof that a renewable energy project would not exist without the funds created by the sale of carbon credits to polluters.

> **❝Here's the ugly truth: nature doesn't care about democracy, or who's right, or what's fair … doing something for the wrong reasons, run by the wrong people, may still save more lives than holding out for a more appealing option.❞**
>
> **Jamais Cascio, writer and futurist**

Controlling the uncontrollable Geo-engineering is a contentious area and anyone proposing anything much more than painting a few roofs white is liable to ridicule at the very least. Moreover, what are some of the potential side effects and who would be liable if something went wrong? What, for instance, would happen in a legal sense if one country implemented an idea and ended up making local weather conditions far worse for a near neighbour? Geoplanetary littering is another issue; local damage to the environment or to local livelihoods yet another. And what happens if an evil foreign power or power-crazed billionaire manages to weaponize one of these technologies?

What, in short, would happen if one country or corporation were able to control the weather? Clearly, natural systems such as climate are highly complex, and attempting to influence them is fraught with difficulty, especially at a technical and political level. However, while complex solutions may be one answer, there are other, much simpler options. Half the world's population now live in cities, for example. While it could be argued that this is part of the problem, in terms of emissions, cities, especially megacities in developing regions – which are being built, or redesigned, from the ground up – also provide a potential solution because they afford opportunities to make housing, transport and infrastructure much more efficient and sustainable.

the condensed idea
Radically re-engineering the planet

11 Megacities

In 1800 about 3 per cent of the world's population was urban. It's currently 50 per cent. By 2050 it will be around 75 per cent. Moreover, many of the cities that will shape the future have hardly been built or, if they have, chances are you've not heard of them. You probably know about Lagos, Jakarta, Dhaka and Karachi, but what about Nouakchott, Douala, Bamako, Ouagadougou, Temuco, Belém or Antananarivo?

Not long ago, many commentators predicted that cities were doomed. People were escaping from metropolises such as New York to live in the relative safety and tranquillity of suburbia. But more recently much of the flow has been in the other direction. For example, between 1990 and 2000 the number of 64–75-year-olds living in downtown Chicago rose by 17 per cent. One reason is that elderly people can feel trapped in rural areas or suburbia, whereas in cities there is always a lot to stimulate the brain and body. A report by the US thinktank the RAND Corporation, for instance, found that suburbanites spend longer in cars, thus reducing fitness and life expectancy. But a far larger force is what's happening in Asia and Africa, where both cities, and their brethren, megacities, are being built and rebuilt.

Growth of the megacity In 1975, there were just three global megacities: New York, Mexico City and Tokyo. Now there are 20-plus, depending on definitions (usually, 10 million-plus people). According to McKinsey, a firm of management consultants, Kinshasa, Lagos, Cairo, São Paulo, Mexico City, Los Angeles, Buenos Aires, Mumbai, Shanghai, Beijing, Delhi, Kolkata and Dhaka all now qualify. Overall, about 20 per cent of the world's population live in around 600 cities, which together generate about 50 per cent of global GDP.

timeline

1800	1950s	2000	2007
3 per cent of the world's people live in cities	83 cities worldwide with populations over 1 million	Population of greater Tokyo area exceeds 35 million	468 cities with populations over 1 million

A very old idea

The oldest company in the world is around 700 years old. The oldest university is about 1,000 years old and the oldest living religion is around 3,500 years old. In contrast, the oldest cities include Jerusalem (5,000) and Jericho (10,500). The reason for this longevity is flexibility. Cities are constantly being knocked down and rebuilt (by about 2 per cent per year) and people are always coming and going, refreshing their energy and creativity. Cities such as London, New York and Tokyo aren't going away. Indeed, they are now being remade and recast as city-states that are economically and culturally ahead of many countries.

Do these cities have anything in common apart from lots of people? At first glance you might think not. Some cities are highly organized, vertical, gleaming and safe, while others are unplanned, dirty, low-rise and dangerous. Beyond these factors, though, large cities do have two basic factors in common.

First, they represent a big problem with regard to climate change and resource management, consuming around 75 per cent of global energy output. However, as we've hinted previously, they could also provide a convenient solution. For example, transport is a key user of energy in urban environments, and city governments are in a strong position to influence how transport in specific and tightly controlled areas is delivered.

Equally, planning regulations mean that city governments can influence how buildings are constructed and how low-carbon and smart technologies are incorporated into large

❝If the city is the world which man created, it is the world in which he is henceforth condemned to live.❞

Robert Park, urban sociologist

2008	2018	2030	2050
Over 50 per cent of humanity lives an urban existence	Detroit declared a 'hollow city' with population falling 20 per cent per year	60 per cent of the world's people live in cities	Half of Africa's population live in cities

infrastructure projects. We'll start to see more low-carbon building materials, increased investment in energy-efficient public transport, more carbon-neutral cities, locally farmed energy and vertical agriculture – literally tower blocks of urban farms that harvest their own power and water and grow food and animals up to 300m (1,000ft) in the air.

The second factor shared by large cities: they act as magnets for human energy. They attract poor people with ambition and put them to productive use, which makes both individuals and cities richer overall. For example, according to Geoffrey West of the Santa Fe Institute (a thinktank), a doubling in size of cities results in a 15 per cent reduction in energy use per capita. But for each doubling, urban dwellers also experience an increase in income of around 15 per cent.

And the more that ambitious individuals move to these areas to secure maximum economic value and become concentrated in small geographic areas, the more people the area attracts. Thus, migration has significant implications for innovation policy because the close proximity of likeminded individuals tends to create a multiplier effect. In other words,

creative cities

According to Professor Richard Florida (author of *The Rise of the Creative Class*), economic progress is primarily driven by ideas, and ideas tend to cluster in large cities that are open and tolerant of diversity. If cities want to become economic powerhouses, they must therefore attract artists, writers, sculptors, musicians, immigrants and assorted oddballs, eccentrics and misfits from other places. In other words, taking a fairly long-term view of urban development, no rock bands, no bohemians and no 'weirdos' equals no significant intellectual property, no scientific breakthroughs, no cutting-edge arts culture and no business model-busting young entrepreneurs.

> **A city is the pulsating product of the human hand and mind, reflecting man's history, his struggle for freedom, creativity, genius and his selfishness and errors.**
>
> **Charles Abrams,** urban expert
> and founder of the New York Housing Authority

what drives economic value and productivity is not where most people live, but where most bright, ambitious and energetic people live, and this tends to be in large global cities.

Pushing out the poorest The problem, of course, is that an influx of high-earning tends to push up property prices, which in turn pushes other individuals out. This reduces overall diversity, and essential services start to suffer because people working in the service support professions cannot afford to live in certain areas.

Love them or loathe them, it seems fairly certain that cities are here to stay and that they will get much bigger in the future. They will also get much smarter, hopefully in terms of the people living in them, but certainly in terms of the way that smart transport and infrastructure are deployed across them, linking individual elements together to create intelligent and to some extent self-aware systems (see Chapter 13).

the condensed idea
More people in big cities

12 Local energy networks

Local power, the idea of producing and distributing electricity in the future from local sources or networks, represents a radical shift in the balance of power away from the fossil fuel and nuclear-run power plants that currently dominate the power industry. The parallel here is perhaps computing, which used to involve gigantic mainframes, but moved to individual PCs, then to mobile devices connected to the Internet.

When you plug in an appliance or a device, there may be thousands of other people doing the same thing at the same time. Central electricity generators have to supply extra power and this is inefficient and costly. Moreover, while large networks benefit from economies of scale, the inefficiencies are significant, especially in terms of transmission leakage and environmental impact. Hence the idea of generating electricity using a local micro-grid or generating whatever energy you need onsite using a variety of hyper-local energy sources.

Small is beautiful Solar cells are one such option, and so too are wind turbines and occasionally water wheels, but there are also innovations such as the bio-gas fermenter, for times when the weather can't be relied upon. The fermenter turns agricultural waste, such as manure and chaff, into methane, which powers an electricity generator. The waste heat from the process is used to heat water for nearby homes. Using these techniques, the German town of Freimant is a model for the future. Not only is it already self-sufficient, but in 2007 it generated a surplus of 2.3 million kilowatt-hours, which it sold back to the national

timeline

1816	1821	1839	1882	1888
First energy company established in USA	First electric motor	Discovery of photovoltaic effect	First hydroelectric power plant	Tesla invents AC alternator

grid. And this is not some commune hoping to shut itself off from the outside world – it is, rather, a modern, and quickly growing, movement. Nor is it simply wresting control out of the hands of the big power companies. Generating power locally is simply more efficient. The average power plant loses 70 per cent of the energy of fossil fuels during the conversion process through heat to the atmosphere or water cooling. The remaining power loses a further 7 per cent from transmission lines.

Presently the large utility companies account for 67 per cent of electricity generated globally. The International Energy Agency's (IEA) World Energy Outlook predicts that even in its alternative scenario (in which governments push hard for energy savings), the large power plants will still account for around 50 per cent of the new power facilities coming online by 2030, while locally generated power will account for just 20 cent.

Energy empowerment

Today, if you try to erect a 9m (30ft) wind turbine in your back garden, chances are that someone won't let you. Solar panels are more acceptable and nobody bats an eyelid if you install an air-conditioning unit on the side of your home. This, however, is changing. For example, 13 million Americans live on plots of land an acre or more in size and windpower companies are targeting them to sell a new generation of home-style wind turbines. Indeed, we are witnessing a significant shift whereby technologies that were once available only for industrial customers (windpower being a classic example) are now being sold to the average Joe in suburbia. The tipping point here is primarily tax credits for the erection of clean technology, but the ability to sell unused power back to a network is also pushing many eco-cynics into previously uncharted territories.

1892	1980	2030	2035	2040
General Electric founded	First US wind farm	Wind farms start to be demolished	Most homes engaged in local energy trading	Personal energy harvesters become mandatory

> **❛In terms of what you can do at the local level for energy efficiency and renewable energy, it's incredible. It's just amazing.❜**
>
> **Joan Fitzgerald,**
> **author of *Emerald Cities***

But there are alternatives, in which governments will have a role to play in breaking the carbon lock-in. Denmark, currently the world's most energy-efficient country, is leading the field in locally generated power. It was the first country to introduce a feed-in tariff, whereby renewable energy producers, even individual households, are paid for the power they produce, and now less than a third of the country's energy comes from big utilities. And Denmark isn't alone. Germany introduced a feed-in tariff in 2004 and is now a world leader in solar power, with 400,000 households and small businesses set up for solar power generation.

Some countries may have trouble getting the big power companies to let go of their stranglehold, but great opportunities for setting up locally generated power can be found in countries in the developing world, where the long-distance power network is still underdeveloped. This may be another example of how areas such as Africa will leapfrog other regions, such as Europe and North America, much as they have done in mobile payments and mobile banking – moving from no landline telephones, desktop computers or laptops in many instances directly to mobiles and smartphones, which many people have been using for a while now to make mobile payments.

Cash cars Another idea is a distributed approach using smart agents that can use batteries already in the home as temporary energy-storage units. These batteries could draw electricity during times of low demand and low price. One remarkable new source may be electric cars. Researchers at the University of Delaware have been running a fleet of seven electric vehicles, known as V2G (vehicle-to-grid), for this purpose. Plugging in a vehicle sends a wireless message to a server and, when the local company needs more energy, it draws it from the vehicle. V2G responds in less than four seconds, compared to the five minutes it would take to boost the generator. Not only that, it generates gross revenue of about $4,000 a year. The wider effect is that pricing could be varied, based on actual demand and cost, and agent systems could buy electricity like a commodity. It could then be stored for use later. If less than half the homes

Consumers and producers

Imagine a future where many of the devices that consume power also create it. Offices, homes and cars can all harvest small amounts of energy, either for themselves or for other devices or people. Individual machines can also be made to 'wake up' in the sense of being made aware of how much energy they are consuming and being programmed only to take power from a local, regional or national network when prices are lowest. But that's just a start. People on the move can be made to harvest energy too, be it kinetic energy from walking around or solar energy harvested by panels on their clothing. The end result would be peer-to-peer energy sharing, where everyone is a producer as well as a consumer of energy.

in the UK were able to use this system, the market would be more stable and households could reduce their bills by 13 per cent, saving some £1.5 billion a year. It's also a thrilling concept that a car could be an income generator, rather than a drain on family finances.

This in turn links to the thought of using hydrogen as a carrier of energy – or as a way of moving power from one physical location to another, much like electricity. A hydrogen-based economy would have enormous future implications, especially with regard to transportation, which is really the crux of the issue when it comes to oil (see Chapter 6).

the condensed idea
Locally produced and distributed energy

13 Smart cities

Stuff that was once 'dumb' is becoming smart. Pipes, roads, buildings and even whole cities are no exception. Whether it's smart meters for water supply, appliances that work out when it's best to be switched on, or dynamic tolling for roads, we can expect more efficiency, less waste, faster fixing and more pricing that's responsive to real-time demand.

Back in the 1990s, David Gelernter, a professor of computer science at Yale University, wrote a book called *Mirror Worlds*. In it he described a world that had a digital reflection. Everything that existed in reality could have a twin in a virtual reality.

Now, thanks to the falling cost and increasing power of computing, the idea is becoming a reality and the real world is converging with the virtual. One example is smart infrastructure. The idea here is to scatter a trillion tiny sensors across the globe to create a ubiquitous sensing network. Such devices would be placed on office buildings, bridges, railways, water pipes, refrigerators and windows to create mountains of data that could help buildings monitor their own energy use or help bridges to find problems and issue warnings to engineers – possibly even to dispatch repair robots to fix their own faults before human operatives even became aware of the problem.

Add a few similar ideas and we'll soon have cities that generate as much electricity as they consume, converting rubbish into energy, diverting heavy traffic automatically and processing sewage to make fuel. Wind cones will help to cool buildings and provide natural lighting, while drinking water will be harvested from rain collected from roofs and walls.

timeline

2000	2009	2018	2020
Building starts on Songdo, a smart city in South Korea	Government sets target of smart water meters in all UK homes by 2020	Energy dashboards made compulsory in European homes	Road pricing for motorways based on real-time traffic conditions

Smart roads

Singapore charges drivers for using popular roads, adjusts traffic lights with traffic flow, uses data collected from taxis to track average driving speeds, and is working on a system that offers parking guidance (cars trying to park is a major cause of congestion). It may also become the first city to introduce dynamic pricing on its roads, according to levels of congestion. Could similar systems work in other areas? How about linking the cost of water not just to the amount used, but to demand? Or offering tax credits or healthcare points to people who walk around a city rather than drive a car?

Changing road use As for roads, thanks to GPS, CCTV and other devices it's easily possible to work out, in real time, how busy roads are and where particular cars are going. This means that vehicles can be charged for entering specific areas or fined for going where they shouldn't. Congestion zones are already popular in some cities, but we should expect the idea to develop much further, with local councils and national governments putting a value on road use and charging road users in real time depending on the time of day, type of car, driving style, speed or

❝**"Smart Growth" is a code word for whatever the user of this term wants to achieve ... "Smart growth" can mean almost anything ... all parties superficially endorse "smart growth" because it is clearly superior to the alternative: "dumb growth".**❞

Anthony Downs, writer

2025	**2030**	**2040**	**2060**
Pavements in Seoul monitor pedestrian traffic and adjust lights automatically	Mobile phones used to control all household appliances remotely	80 per cent of the world's buildings replicated in virtual worlds	Dustbin collection disappears, replaced with pressure-driven pipes

> ❛The bias lurking behind every large-scale smart city is a belief that bottom-up complexity can be bottled and put to use for top-down ends.❜
>
> **Greg Lindsay, Rudin Center for Transportation Policy and Management, New York University**

volume of traffic. Payment will commence the second you turn a wheel onto a public road, although automated charging will probably start with motorways and slowly trickle down through ever-lesser roads until one day the technology ends up outside your own front door.

Currently, most individuals pay for roads through fuel taxation or vehicle registration. However, such schemes aren't very smart and someone who drives infrequently can end up paying almost as much as a heavy user. In theory, charging drivers per mile or per minute is a better idea, although don't expect the other forms of charging to disappear. In the Netherlands the government had devised a plan to charge all road users on a per-kilometre basis by 2012. This idea has been scrapped for the time being, but similar ideas are likely to return sooner or later. Why? For one thing, in one road test, 70 per cent of drivers changed their behaviour due to such charging. In the future, expect to see not only more road pricing in real time, but also more pricing based upon car type and use. For example, it would not be difficult to design a system whereby the cost of driving is directly related to the number of occupants or even the purpose of the journey.

Home economics And don't think that the inside of your own home will be immune from such technology either. We've already seen digital dashboards that monitor energy use migrating from industrial buildings to private homes and there's no reason to suspect that automation will stop there. So how about clothing that's equipped with RFID tags (see page 5) so that your clothes can talk to your washing machine and work out the most efficient time to connect with the water pipes and power grids? Or how about a bathroom mirror (that's also a TV) which uses facial recognition to identify individual family members and adjust the diary, to-do list or TV channels accordingly? Or what about bathroom scales that can talk to your fridge to stop you opening it if you've eaten too much pizza the night before.

This will all happen, in part, but the shift from dumb devices to smarter stuff won't end there. We will increasingly use smart mobile phones and other mobile devices to monitor our immediate surroundings and even our own health. For example, elderly people could be monitored at home and doctors called only when they are needed – or small children could be monitored

Wind forecasting

The European Union wants to source 20 per cent of its electricity from renewable sources, largely windpower, by the year 2020. China has increased its windpower target to 100 GW by 2020. Globally, $14 billion was invested in wind farms in the first three months of 2010. But without a clear idea of where and when the wind will blow in the years to come, such commitments look airy. The production of wind is a largely local affair as the immediate topographical environment influences how much wind is created. Currently, measurement of wind conditions is dependent upon samples of wind taken at proposed wind-energy sites, overlaid with wind data from the nearest official meteorological site. In the future there will be growing interest in the art and science of wind forecasting. However, unless the industry can be made profitable without government subsidies we may one day be pulling turbines down faster than they are currently going up.

24/7 so that they didn't get lost or get into trouble. In other words, rather than spending billions developing sensors, why not simply tap into the 5 billion-plus mobile phones currently roaming the Earth and use people themselves (or at least the cameras, microphones and GPS that they're walking around with) as the sensing network? At some point we will then decide that trying to get little children to carry a smartphone isn't practical and we will simply smartchip children at birth. We do this with pets so why not people?

Thus, in the future, we'll see currently inert objects imbued with some sense of where they are and what they're doing and we'll use such information to make cities, and the things they contain, more efficient.

the condensed idea
Cities that can think

14 Next-generation transport

Several of China's largest cities boast all-electric bus fleets and it's conceivable that the country will soon become the world's first all-electric automotive nation. Meanwhile, aircraft manufacturers are experimenting with hybrid-electric engines, so could it one day be the end of the road – and the runway – for conventional forms of wheeled (and winged) transport?

It seems unlikely that we'll give up our cars in the near future, but the way we buy, fuel and use them will change radically. Some experts believe more than 80 per cent of cars worldwide will be electric by 2050. Such cars will feature hybrid-gas or biofuelled engines that kick in after 18–24km (30–40 miles) of silent electric motoring, spinning a generator that will extend the range of the battery. New motors will be slim and light, allowing them to be wheel-mounted. However, despite such innovations, petrol-fuelled cars will remain popular for many years to come by combining a broad range of new ideas, from ultra-lightweight parts to immensely efficient engines and navigation systems.

Nevertheless, if you want a glimpse of what the future of four-wheeled transport might look like, Riversimple – a UK company that has designed a hydrogen-powered car – is illuminating and certainly inspirational. Rather than buying the car outright, owners lease a vehicle and the cost includes the price of locally produced hydrogen. Moreover, the aim is to make all the cars, and a pool of different types of vehicle, available locally.

timeline

1769	1885	1960s	2004
First self-propelled mechanical vehicle	Karl Benz invents the modern motorcar	Personal jetpack technology becomes a reality	China unveils a high-speed magnetic levitation train

There are sceptics, of course. With most electric and hybrid cars, the lithium-ion battery needs improvement, particularly the safety aspects of overcharging and discharging. People also need to be persuaded to spend more on their cars now to save money in the future. Plus, not every driver has a garage where they can plug into the mains overnight, so the network of charging points needs to expand.

If I had asked people what they wanted, they would have said faster horses.

Henry Ford, founder of Ford Motor Company

What's driving new solutions? Nevertheless, new technologies may yet get us out of some old-fashioned jams. General Motors, for example, has a vision of the future consisting of remote-controlled convoys of vehicles telling each other what they're doing in order to avoid accidents and congestion and to improve convenience and fuel efficiency. Instead of big, thirsty cars, it features small vehicles plugged into electric – and wireless – networks. It predicts that people will be relieved from the hassle of driving and have more free time behind the wheel. Indeed, we are drawing closer to a radical re-imagining of the private driving experience, where people will get the journey they are willing to pay for.

Putting on the brakes

Departments of Transport in various countries are looking at Intelligent Speed Adaptation (ISA) as a way of reducing road accidents. The system works by linking digital speed maps and GPS to a computer in your car, which in turn applies the brake or blocks acceleration. Early trials have indicated that accidents could be reduced by 20 per cent if all vehicles were fitted with this technology. The system is likely to appear in buses and taxis first and may then be applied to private cars.

2016	2022	2039	2036
35 per cent of cars now hybrids	Self-driving cars start to appear in China and India	High-speed rail networks link Europe with North Africa	Solar-powered planes widely used in Africa and Australia

For example, why can't traffic signals communicate directly with cars and why shouldn't GPS be used to control the speed of, and distance between cars, lorries and buses in a traffic lane automatically? If road conditions are treacherous, why can't acceleration or top speeds be automatically capped? And how is it remotely possible to have a vehicle go missing in this day and age? Why can't location tracking be sold as standard, along with a facility to immobilize the vehicle and call the police if it's stolen. And why can't our cars read out our emails and let us dictate a reply?

Electric planes

Are electric and hybrid airliners the shape of wings to come? The airline industry is under pressure to become greener, but most current solutions offer little more than marginal improvements. Biofuels and hydrogen could make an impact, but both suffer from supply constraints, among other issues. So how about powering a plane with an electric motor? Small planes are light enough to take off under electric power, but large commercial aircraft cannot. The problem lies primarily with the batteries. A conventional 200-seater plane would need 3,000 tons of lithium-ion batteries. But there are solutions on the distant horizon, including the use of jet fuel for take-off and climb, then ecofriendly electric power for cruising (precisely where fossil fuels do most of their damage).

'Home, James' The big question, though, is when are we finally going to get behind the wheel of a driverless vehicle? Well you already can. Many airports already feature driverless trains. Indeed, much of the technology needed for driverless cars already exists. Radar cruise control, motion sensors, lane-change warnings, electronic stability control, and digital mapping are all here. The main obstacle is regulation, liability laws and our own feelings about letting go of the steering wheel.

And if this makes you feel unsafe, how about pilotless commercial airliners? Again, the technology exists, but our historically conditioned brains can't quite cope with the idea yet. The main argument for a move to driverless vehicles (including planes) is safety.

But the impact of technology doesn't end there. With parking, for example, experiments are already underway to introduce wireless sensor networks that will hopefully put an end to city parking issues and traffic problems. The system works through a series of small plastic sensors, one of which is attached to each metered parking spot. When the sensors are

> ❝*New Scientist* magazine reported that in the future, cars could be powered by hazelnuts. That's encouraging, considering an eight-ounce jar of hazelnuts costs about nine dollars.❞
>
> **Jimmy Fallon,** actor and comedian

linked via the network, the result is a real-time database of parking-spot vacancies. This information can be displayed to drivers through displays on street signs or available through the screens on smartphones. It's estimated that drivers searching for on-street parking make up as much as 30 per cent of traffic in central business districts, so this is a good idea.

The bottom line here is that many of the strains of driving will be removed in the future, with much of the control handed over to the vehicle. All of the signs currently indicate that in the future we'll see time-slots on motorways prebooked to avoid congestion and there will be an increase in car-pooling, with reduced tolls to provide incentives, and onboard software that will direct drivers to the location of others wanting to car-pool. Increased robotization of the car and a greater dependence on satellite navigation will allow motorists to use their travel time for leisure or work activities such as reading newspapers or making use of in-car games.

As well as making the trip more enjoyable for passengers, it's hoped that handing the control over to the vehicle will prove cleaner, safer and more efficient. Cars will not start if the driver, who will be recognized by an iris scan, does not have a licence or is unauthorized to drive that particular car. Public transport will enter a renaissance era thanks to costs and, most importantly, convenience and energy efficiency. Eventually, all buses and trains will become driverless and so too, one day, will all planes.

the condensed idea
Reinventing our wheels

15 Extra-legal & feral slums

According to a UN estimate, 1 in 7 people worldwide now live in slums and in many cases these slums, which are not regulated or sanctioned by law, are set to become major cities in the near future. Meanwhile, some urban areas have become so lawless that authorities have all but given up on removing criminal gangs and have fallen back on a policy of geographical containment instead.

There has been a lot of comment and concern about failed states and feral children of late, so it should come as no surprise that feral cities are set to become a future threat to organized society and civil order.

An article by Peter Liotta and James Miskel in *World Policy Journal* (US), for instance, makes the point that Mogadishu, in Somalia, could be the model for future cities in many parts of the world in the sense of creating a series of 'non-traditional' security threats. In other words, instead of worrying about terrorist incursions from abroad, demented dictators or rogue states, we should be worrying more about the threats from within, especially the possibility of very high levels of unemployment and social exclusion creating highly alienated groups in very specific and highly concentrated geographical locations, especially in cities. Apart from Mogadishu, other cities with the potential to become lawless or feral include Johannesburg, São Paulo, Mexico City and Karachi. This is largely due to high levels of organized crime, high rates of unemployment (feeding the criminality) and politicians and law enforcement that either will not or cannot resolve the problem.

timeline

2012	2014	2022
Parents hire private security guards to escort teenagers in London	25 per cent more helipads in São Paulo than New York due to no-go areas	CEO of General Electric visits outskirts of Nairobi to learn about recycling

Inside a feral city What does a feral city look like? Much like an ordinary city in many cases, although the authorities, and especially the police, have usually abandoned large areas of the city (potentially the whole city) in favour of outlaw landlords, drug barons and other criminals who either fight each other or make life unpleasant and generally dangerous for the non-criminally minded. As you might imagine, such areas are usually collapsing physically as well as morally.

❝If the young men are not initiated into the village, they will burn it down just to feel its warmth.❞
African proverb

In cities such as Cairo and Bogata, the number of people living 'off the books' and out of reach of the formal authorities may exceed the numbers living in formally planned developments. According to some estimates, most of the global population growth in the past two or three decades has taken place in such areas and much of the world's future population growth is expected to occur there.

What are the implications for the people within these cities? For one thing, a series of problems when trying to allocate food, water, healthcare

Slums of the future

According to Richard Rogers, one of Britain's leading architects, the rush to build 3 million new homes across England by the year 2020 is resulting in architecture that looks indistinguishable from projects from Beijing to Buenos Aires. Are we therefore building the slums of tomorrow? Part of the problem is rootlessness – a lack of clear provenance and identity – but the problem is also related to the time it takes to plan and build major developments or redevelopments. For example, London's Terminal 5, which opened a few years ago at Heathrow airport, was being discussed 19 years ago.

2026	2030	2070
Indian rubbish pricing and distribution system copied in USA	Soldiers outnumber police on some city streets	After the collapse of the mines, Western Australia becomes a prison colony

and transport resources. Water is an especially tricky problem and access to fresh supplies often costs more in slums than it does in smarter districts of the same city. In some cases, water for drinking, bathing and cleaning can account for half of a poor family's income.

There is also the serious issue of rubbish disposal and pollution, which, along with high-density living, can cause outbreaks of disease. Other disasters, ranging from building collapses to mud slides, can also be made much worse due to a combination of unregulated design, bad materials, and the fact that much of the land on which these dwellings are built is of very poor quality, often alongside river banks or on steep hillsides. Moreover, when extreme wealth lives side by side with extreme poverty, as happens in many cities, including London and New York, this may facilitate not only petty but also organized crime.

People power But it's not all bad news. If governments or aid agencies cannot provide food, water, shelter or other necessities, people will often organize these things for themselves. Moreover, as the American writer Stewart Brand has commented, adversity can breed inventiveness, especially ways of collaborating at a local level. Brand also points out

What if?

It's the future. Crime is totally out of control in a handful of urban areas and the police are totally powerless to help. What could happen next? One scenario is that the army works alongside the police, which has more or less happened before, in Northern Ireland, for example. Another scenario is that the government erects a large wall or fence around the whole area. Nobody is allowed in or out. Ridiculous? Probably. Impossible? Possibly not. If crime in specific areas reaches epidemic proportions it might at some point make more sense to turn the whole area into an informal prison rather than attempting to identify, then export troublemakers to secure facilities elsewhere. Other possibilities might include the tagging on all residents by postcode or perhaps once again building prison ships or creating prison countries.

❝Traditionally, problems of urban decay and associated issues, such as crime, have been seen as domestic issues best dealt with by internal security or police forces. That will no longer be an option.❞

Richard Norton, Naval War College Review

that informal cities can reduce fertility, in some instances by encouraging women to enter education or find paid work, which benefits not only the individual, but the nation as a whole.

And let's not forget that when it comes to the utilization of scarce resources, those living in informal cities in countries such as India can usually teach wasteful Westerners a thing or two about materials reuse, recycling and reduction.

Rather than flatten informal cities, perhaps governments should learn to identify, then develop democratically elected city leaders and urban entrepreneurs to show the rest of the world how to live more efficiently and economically. This is not an excuse to tolerate slums or urban poverty and decay, but it does mean that we should always try to maintain a more positive mindset about their potential. Critically, in some parts of the world, we should also stop automatically linking material comfort with perceived levels of happiness, because in some instances those living with next to nothing materially are considerably better off mentally and spiritually than those who appear to have everything.

the condensed idea
Slums the size of cities

16 An internet of things

According to Cisco Systems, there will be 50 billion 'things' connected to the Internet by 2020. That's seven for every man, woman and child on the planet. So what are some of these 'things' and what are the consequences of an Internet that's increasingly made up of physical objects embedded with sensors?

In the future your socks will have an IP address and your sock drawer will know how many pairs you've got and what colour they are. In other words, barcodes and RFID (see page 5) tags were only the first small steps towards a world where information is embedded within everyday objects, which are connected to networks so that they can communicate with each other and with the network as a whole. This will mean that the precise identity, location and status of everything – and possibly everyone – can be identified, and future actions or conditions can be predicted.

In this future world, physical and virtual objects start to merge and each is augmented either by its physical form or by a digital presence. For example, every real building might have a complete digital replica right down to individual door handles, which can then be communicated with to access information about when the features were installed, and by whom, as well as how often they've been used or what a typical failure rate might be.

Virtual objects and environments will therefore gain 'real' identities – even personalities – while physical objects and environments will have digital replicas or twins. This will allow one to communicate with the other, to

timeline

2008	2011	2014	2020
School blazers with embedded GPS linked to an SMS facility in Japan	Adidas launches football boots that analyse performance	Sensors added to buildings enable the harvesting of hyper-local climate data	Global Internet penetration reaches 6 billion

experience the wider external environment, which in some instances will trigger certain actions or events.

After that, everything will be linked to a single brain – the network – at which point the machine will know more about us than we know about it and we will delegate responsibility for our lives to the machine. It will be all-knowing and all-seeing, which will mean radical shifts in transparency and privacy. This is also an ambient-information environment, where almost anything can be accessed from anywhere.

At the extreme, events will happen automatically and collaboratively around us without conscious individual intervention or thought. For example, imagine a world where computers sense exactly what

> **❝I used to tell jokes about Internet-enabled light bulbs. I can't tell jokes about it anymore – there already is an Internet-connected light bulb.❞**
>
> **Vint Cerf, VP and Chief Internet Evangelist at Google**

Service denied

In 2004, the Pew Internet & American Life Project conducted a survey about the future of the Internet that tapped into the brains of 1,200 technology experts, academics and industry gurus. The results were far from conclusive: 42 per cent of experts thought that civic involvement would increase over the next decade due to the Internet, but almost 30 per cent disagreed. However, there were two points on which most of the respondents agreed at the time. The first was that traditional publishing, news and media organizations would be transformed by the Internet over the next few years (they were right). The second was that there would be a 'devastating attack' on the Internet (infrastructure) within the next decade. This has yet to happen but they still have until 2014 to be proven right.

2030	**2052**	**2066**	**2077**
90 billion devices connected to the Internet	The day the world stops (first major network failure)	Every tree has its own IP address	Disconnecting from the network becomes an offence

> **The Internet of Things is also triggering new questions on ownership and consumption ... we grow into an access-based economy, where IOI makes a pay-what-you-use system possible on an individual level.**
>
> **Alexander Bassi,** Institute for Internet and Society

mood you're in and predict what you need, whether it's adjusting the air-conditioning, making tea or turning off the lights after you leave a room.

Changing perspective One concern here is obviously what happens if (when) there is a system crash, because each wave of computing makes us more dependent than ever on computers.

The solution will probably be even more technology, which is not what many people will want to hear, especially anyone familiar with E.M. Forster's novel *The Machine Stops*. Perhaps the best way to think about the Internet in the future is to see it as something that you no longer 'do', but as something that simply 'is'. When this happens the Internet will seem to have vanished.

The Internet of things is not quite the same as ubiquitous or pervasive computing, but like most things in the future it's connected. In the past, information was scarce and tended to be tightly controlled by governments or large corporations. Moreover, the flow was generally in one direction (certainly with media, which was broadcast to relatively passive recipients), and feedback loops (either from bottom upwards or from outside to in) were slow and ponderous.

Wealth of data But this is changing and will change even faster in the future when previously inert objects can both generate and respond to information in real time. In this world, everything becomes data, which enables previously unimaginable amounts of automation and intelligence. For instance, how about a light bulb that knows where it is and where

One in the eye for glaucoma

Perhaps the idea that one day computers with wireless connectivity will become so small and so cheap that they are embedded in absolutely everything from toothbrushes to lipstick seems a little implausible? Well it's started already. Scientists have developed a computer the size of a grain of sand that contains a microprocessor, solar panel, pressure sensor and wireless connectivity. What's it for? Glaucoma sufferers can place the computer in their eye and it measures the pressure of liquid on the eyeball, sending data for analysis to a hospital wirelessly.

it comes from and can automatically order an exact replacement when it nears the end of its life? Or a fridge that knows what's inside it, which dishes can be made using its contents and what needs to be eaten up or thrown out in the next two days?

But that's just the mundane stuff. Once computers become small enough and cheap enough we won't be able to resist adding them to absolutely everything. The only real unknowns are what exactly we – or the machines – will do with the vast amounts of data that will be produced and whether or not the networks that control everything will be open or closed or will one day 'wake up' in the sense of being self-aware. It certainly makes you view Google in a whole new light.

the condensed idea
Everything will connect

17 Quantum & DNA computing

Computer processing speeds and storage capacities have grown astonishingly over the past 50 years, but computer evolution is starting to run up against physical limits. Moore's Law, which dates from 1965, states that computing power (transistor density) doubles every 18 months or so, but how can such growth continue to occur without hitting the fundamentals of physics?

Computers currently operate using an electrical charge to manipulate bits that exist in one of two states: 0 or 1. Quantum computers, on the other hand, are not so restricted. They encode information as a 0 and a 1 simultaneously using principles of quantum mechanics such as superposition and entanglement. This means that instead of working on one computation after another (albeit at very fast speeds) a quantum computer can work on different computations at the same time. Hey presto, a computer with processing speeds a million or more times faster than anything that's currently available, but more importantly, a computer able to solve problems that conventional computers cannot – for example, pattern recognition or code-breaking.

Quantum computing also has another major advantage. With conventional, silicon-based computers, overheating and energy use is a major problem. With quantum computers it's not. Do such computers currently exist? At the moment the answer is no, certainly in the sense of being commercially scalable, usable or practical. But it's a reasonably safe bet to say that they will.

timeline

*c.*100 BC	1837	2015	2020
Antikythera mechanism (early analogue mechanical computer)	Charles Babbage describes analytical engine	Direct brain-to-machine computer interfaces	Computer games beamed to the human brain

Living computers?

And if you think that sounds a bit far-fetched, how about DNA (deoxyribonucleic acid) computing? Again, the current problem is the physical limits of speed and miniaturization imposed by the use of silicon chips to power computers. But what if we used bio-chips made from living organisms to create subatomic circuitry, rather than relying on silicon made from silica sand – essentially, silicon chips are made by melting down ordinary sand into ingots and slicing these into tiny wafers, which are then treated and engineered in various ways.

More of everything

Moore's Law is named after Gordon Moore, one of the co-founders of computer-chip maker Intel. He wrote a briefing note back in 1965 stating that the number of individual elements of a computer chip had doubled each year between 1958 and 1965 and was set to do the same for at least a further decade. This observation (widely quoted as a prediction) has held more or less true ever since, and the number of transistors that can be put onto an integrated circuit doubles every 18–36 months. However, in recent years the speed of development is starting to slow thanks to the physical limitations of current materials.

Believe it or not, the potential already exists to build the next generation of computers using DNA molecules. Our own bodies currently act like super-computers in the sense that our DNA permanently stores information about us. Therefore, it's probably possible to develop computers that store, retrieve and process data trillions of times faster than anything with which we're currently familiar. DNA, currently an area of immense interest and intense research, links with other hugely promising fields such as nanobiology and biomolecular engineering and is broadly

❝Just look at computer memory – in the early 1970s one megabyte cost more than a house, now it costs less than a piece of candy.❞

Gilles Thomas, ST Microelectronics

2025	2040	2050	2070
Computers injected into the human body	Human beings no longer need to remember anything	Internet-enabled telepathy	People able to record and share dreams

characterized as using or manipulating materials at a nano (i.e.1–100 nanometres) scale. (See Chapter 18 for more about the future potential of nanotechnology or for an explanation of just how tiny a nanometre really is.)

How might we make use of some of these aforementioned developments in everyday life? One application that's nanotechnology-based and already on the cusp of making an impact is Magnetoresistive Random-Access Memory (MRAM), which would store pictures almost instantly. In the future, phones or cameras might enter this realm. In a few years, similar technology will enable your computer to start up or switch off in a thousandth of a second rather than what often feels like an eternity to some nowadays.

Of course, computers already exist in our own bodies on another level. Wetware is a term often used to describe the interaction between the human brain and the central nervous system. It refers partly to the electrical and chemical nature of the brain and partly to the interaction between our neurons (our hardware, if you like) and the impulses, which are like software. Or perhaps the mind is software and everything else is hardware? As we'll see later, this is controversial.

> **The age of computing has not even begun. What we have today are tiny toys not much better than an abacus. The challenge is to approach the fundamental laws of physics as closely as we can.**
>
> **Stan Williams, Hewlett-Packard**

Future potential What will we use these superfast, supersmall and supercheap computers to do? Hopefully not just playing *Angry Birds*! We could instantly look at 250,000 emails and extract the two most important messages. Or perhaps we'll watch movies via our contact lenses? Maybe we'll just digitally record and store everything that happens in front of our eyes from birth to death (or maybe governments will).

Perhaps these computers will run cities or potentially the whole planet. Maybe they'll be able to write a sonnet like Shakespeare or paint like Picasso. Maybe we'll use them to encrypt sensitive data, predict the weather or find a cure for cancer. None of this is likely to be that far away given the speed of some developments in and around computing and artificial intelligence (see Chapter 20, for instance).

A test tube that thinks

In 1994 a scientist in the USA came up with the idea of using DNA in a test to solve a complicated mathematical problem. If this sounds ridiculous, think of your own body, which uses biochemical reactions to operate your brain, which is then able to think up ideas such as how to create a biochemical computer. Forward to 2002, and Israeli scientists announced the creation of a DNA or biomolecular computer using chemical reactions in a liquid solution instead of silicon chips and electrons. The result was a machine that ran 100,000 times faster than any comparable PC at the time. Furthermore, they can be minuscule – a trillion of them would be about the same size as a single drop of water and could possibly sit inside one.

Having said all this, there is one question that won't go away. If we invent new quantum and DNA computers to generate massive amounts of data, how will the Internet infrastructure – or our old-fashioned biological brains – cope? If we do manage to continue doubling the power of computers every 18 months, which some people maintain is quite possible using quantum and DNA computers, then in a decade computers will be 100 times more powerful than anything we've got today. In 25 years that number becomes 100,000. At this point our data will take on a life of its own. We will have more machines and algorithms that talk with each other and our most important concern will be trying to explain to machines what it means to be human.

the condensed idea
Next-stage computing

18 Nanotechnology

This is the science of manipulating matter at an atomic or subatomic scale (1–100 nanometres) to create supersmart materials with entirely new properties or to manufacture objects at an atomically precise level. How small is a nanometre? It's a billionth of a metre. How small is that? A human hair is roughly 100,000 nanometres wide.

The digital revolution is well underway, but there is potentially another, more powerful, revolution just around the corner. Nanotechnology could be profoundly transformative, radically reshaping modern manufacturing and potentially affecting distribution, retailing and environmental concerns too. Indeed, nanotech could be as important as the steam engine, the transistor and the Internet combined.

Tiny factories of the future Modern manufacturing (and to some extent global capitalism) has been founded on the belief that large inputs are required and that economies of scale produce economic benefit. This won't necessarily be the case in the future. Products could in theory be assembled using atomically precise nanotechnology 'factories', which will be exceedingly small. So small in fact that they could in theory be built inside people's homes. Moreover, thanks to nanotechnology, products could be created only for the period in which they're needed and then be reverse-manufactured to get rid of them. What does this actually mean? Think of the way in which products made of metal can be easily melted down and reused or turned into something else. Nanomanufacturing would be much the same – except returning nanomade products to their constituent parts would mean disassembling them back into atoms.

timeline

2020	2025	2040	2042
Hugely efficient solar energy using new nanomaterials	Nanotechnology materials used in 35 per cent of consumer products	Computers billions of times faster than anything currently available	Claytronic products make commercial debut

Personal Manufacturing Units (PMUs) would be able to assemble anything people wanted, much like a 3D printer. Again, the big difference is that the inputs will be atoms, not physical materials as we're used to them. So if you want a new set of eight blue plates for a dinner party, they could be assembled in your own PMU. Thus, transport, logistics, inventory, waste disposal and retail all disappear right in front of your eyes. This ushers in a whole new economic system that is less reliant on physical resources and human labour. In other words, we no longer experience physical constraints.

By combining nanotechnology with robotics and computing, we can create 'things' that can change into other 'things'. This is the emergent field of claytronics, whereby three-dimensional objects can be turned into

> **The best scientist is open to experience ... the idea that anything is possible.**
>
> **Ray Bradbury,** sci-fi writer

3D printing

In the late 1700s and early 1800s, the Industrial Revolution created mass production, which in turn allowed economies of scale and turned both business and society upside down. So too, 3D printing (also known as fabbing) – is in one sense a very early and very crude version of atomically precise manufacturing, and it could turn everything upside down once again by making it as cheap to produce one of something as it is to produce many. How does it work? Think of it like a computer printer, but instead of printing pages or flat images using ink, you 'print' 3D objects, ranging from a pair of shoes or a new chair to tables or aircraft parts, by adding consecutive layers of liquid, which then hardens. Does this exist already? Yes, in a crude form.

2046	2050	2065	2099
Ford introduce cars that can change colour	First commercially available PMU unveiled	Common foodstuffs assembled via nanotech, not grown naturally	Elimination of 99 per cent of diseases

other three-dimensional objects – a boat into a car or even a large beef sandwich (shades of *Transformers* meets *SpongeBob SquarePants*). Or fully realistic human replicants that allow individuals to be in more than one place at once and converse either with real people or their programmable clones. Fully programmable matter essentially. Still not freaked out? Then how about an army of tiny self-assembling, self-aware robots that decide human beings have had enough fun and that it's time for us to leave now.

Life-changing technology This is all a long way off, and may never happen at all. In the meantime, we will use nanotech to develop socks that will never need washing, suits that repel pollen, stain-resistant carpets, fully interactive digital curtains, self-cleaning windows, bulletproof suits, anti-microbial food packaging or wallpaper that changes pattern, colour and scent depending on the season. Some of these ideas are here already – self-cleaning glass, for instance – but you can almost guarantee that the best is yet to come and that many of the things we'll invent 10, 20 or even 50 years hence will make even the most cynical eyes pop out on stalks.

We'll see bridges made of materials with fundamentally different properties at different points along the bridge (down to each millimetre or less – so that it would have differing strengths, or move differently, at various

It's 2037 ...

You have a brain tumour, which just a few years earlier surgeons would have pronounced inoperable. Fortunately, scientists have now developed a range of microscopic robots that can be injected into your bloodstream and can swim through your body using tiny piezoelectric micro-motors to reach the source of the problem. They administer various life-saving treatments including drug delivery and microscopic surgery to highly sensitive areas deep inside the human brain. Once the treatment has been successfully completed the tiny bots are programmed with a form of satnav to find their way down one of the body's existing exit routes and are disposed of in the usual manner.

points) and many new materials that are much stronger and lighter than anything that's currently available – for use as vast windows on giant passenger aircraft, for example. Airbus Industries have already created a vision of a future plane featuring a bionic element that mimics the bone structure of birds. It's coated with a transparent biopolymer membrane, which eliminates the need for windows. Even the floors of such an aircraft could be made transparent using nanotechnology.

> **❝On the molecular scale, you find it's reasonable to have a machine that does a million steps per second, a mechanical system that works at computer speeds.❞**
>
> Eric Drexler, **engineer and author**

Such technology also promises to revolutionize medicine. An early example is the use of nanoparticles to treat disorders ranging from rheumatoid arthritis to cystic fibrosis. It's likely that the first area of nanomedicine really to take off will be cancer treatments, due to the ability of nanoparticles to get inside the actual tumour cells and change them (hence drugs that are more potent but less toxic). Nanocapsules are already available for the treatment of ovarian and breast cancers, but these deliver drugs only to the neighbourhood of cancer cells rather than to the individual cells, which will be a significant development.

As Eric Drexler, one of the pioneers in the field of nanotechnology, has observed: 'After realizing that we would eventually be able to build molecular machines that could arrange atoms to form virtually any pattern that we wanted, I saw that an awful lot of consequences followed from that.' I'd say that's something of an understatement.

the condensed idea
Terribly tiny technology

19 Gamification

Increasingly, organizations are turning to gamification: the application of online gaming techniques, such as gaining points or status, to engage the attention or alter the behaviour of individuals or communities. Wearable devices linked to game-like systems could, for instance, induce overweight people to take more exercise or eat healthy foods.

Gamification works on three principles: First, people can be competitive (with themselves and with others). Second, people will share certain kinds of information. Third, people like to have fun and be rewarded. That's why if you regularly buy a coffee at your local coffee shop you might end up with a nice badge courtesy of a social networking company such as foursquare. And that's perhaps why, if you drink enough coffee at the same place, you might be crowned the coffee shop king – for a day. Or there's Chore Wars, where people battle the washing-up in return for virtual points or avatar energy boosts.

These are mundane examples, but there are better ones. Life Circle is a mobile app that allows blood banks to keep track of where potential blood donors are in real time. Clever, but the really smart bit is that blood donors can synchronize this with social networks to potentially engage in a bit of competitive activity over who's given the most blood or who's donated most often. Endomondo is another example, allowing users to track their workouts, challenge their friends and analyse their training.

Similar techniques might be employed in the future to encourage people to fill in tax returns, stop smoking, give up drugs, remember to take their drugs, drink less, walk more, vote, sleep, remain married, use

timeline

2016	2018	2021
Farmville announces its billionth player	The Indian PM offers voters points for policy ideas	The UK's National Health Service launches a 'beat cancer' game

contraception, cycle, recycle or revise for exams. Education, for example, especially in the early years, is all about goals, points, scores and prizes, so why not leverage a few online tricks to improve exam results or to switch students into less popular educational courses or institutions? Farmville running nursery services? It's not impossible.

> **❝The future is a video game.❞**
>
> **Angelina Chapin,**
> **writer and journalist**

According to Gartner, a respected information technology research and consulting firm, more than 50 per cent of companies will add gamification techniques to their innovation processes by 2015. Deloitte, one of the top four professional services firms, has named gamification as one of its major technology trends, and M2, a research firm, has predicted that American companies will spend $2.8 billion on gamification by the year 2016. There is, of course, a danger that anything hyped to this extent will soon crash and burn, but in the meantime expect gamification design to emerge as a highly sought-after skill. Also expect cash-strapped governments, in

Real life is not a game

It's true that gaming offers people social benefits they might not receive in real life. These include gift giving, reciprocity and rituals. But can games really tap into deep social needs to create practical change for the better? One example is the video game *World Without Oil,* in which people collaboratively suggest solutions to a real-world issue. The difficulty with this perspective, however, is that life doesn't have strict rules, rewards and goals in the way that a game does. In the real world, there are vastly conflicting desires and priorities (grain to eat versus ethanol for the car) and life is more like a system of complex, interlinked games than one game.

2030	**2040**	**2050**
Foursquare appointed to run early-years education in South Korea	US Department of Energy announces a game called Energy Smackdown	The Catholic Church replaces confession with a mobile gaming app

> ⁶⁶**Games are a compromise between
> intimacy and keeping intimacy away.**⁹⁹
>
> **Eric Berne, psychiatrist and author**

particular, to embrace gamification as a further way to nudge people in the direction of certain choices, especially those relating to individual decisions about healthcare provision and retirement savings.

Scratching the surface How could anyone possibly have a problem with this? Surely this is a fairly harmless activity? Making everything fun and social is simply a way to get people, especially younger people, to do things they don't really want to do or haven't really thought about doing. Just a way of tapping into the fact that hundreds of millions of people spend billions of hours playing online games and feel pretty good about themselves both during and after. Simply a way of getting people to make the right choices in terms of looking after themselves and their future. Why not use this desire for competition, recognition and respect to increase participation in new product trials or boost the loyalty of voters towards your particular brand of government?

The answer to this is that turning the world into a game benefits certain interest groups. For example, if you can get people to do things for you for status or feelings of accomplishment, you may not have to pay other people to do it instead. In other words, your harmless game play is actually adding to the unemployment queue. Moreover, cynical observers might point to the fact that if activities are designed to produce 80 per cent positive outcomes along with 20 per cent near-misses, then what happens to resilience? Perhaps it is all OK if people are taught to understand why they have missed their goals ('failure' won't be a word that's used very often), but one still wonders what endless positive reinforcement will do to people – and to society as a whole – over the longer term. Maybe this won't be an issue because gamification will be deliberately designed to become so addictive that people won't notice what's really going on.

Similarly, getting users to co-create or co-filter products or services or act as data-entry clerks by offering virtual rewards or status also means that companies won't have to put time and effort into improving inferior products or services themselves. Moreover, it seems infantile to treat all customers and citizens as though they are animated superheroes on a secret mission to save the planet. Isn't a virtual badge – or a real one for that matter – a rather superficial substitute for real-life engagement with other human beings?

Instant praise

Yammer is a private social network that's used by companies such as Ford Motor Company and LG to share knowledge and to solve problems. One feature is something called the Yammer Praise app, which is a way of publicly praising or recognizing colleagues. To use the function, all employees have to do is pick a preselected icon (a thumbs-up icon, for instance) and add a message to say thank you or to indicate why it's being used. In the future, perhaps nobody will say thank you face-to-face or send you a thoughtful one-off handwritten note. You'll just get a gold star or a smiley face, like you did back in primary school.

Smart or sinister? On one level, gamification is a smart tool to encourage people to do what's in their best interest over the longer term. On the other hand, it can be seen as a manipulative way of getting individuals to conform to a subjective set of rules or goals or suit short-term commercial interests or to secretly collect data about user behaviour or location.

What if, for instance, participation in certain games was to become mandatory? Gamification started in the media, then spread to fitness, but what if health and well-being applications are indeed embraced by governments (or private medical insurance companies), which remove access to certain services unless individuals reach certain 'levels' or targets?

the condensed idea
Using games
to alter behaviour

20 Artificial Intelligence

In 1956, an American computer scientist named John McCarthy coined the term 'Artificial Intelligence' (AI). He envisaged an age of intelligent machines that he thought would be reality within a decade. Fast forward to the early part of the 21st century and true AI still seems a very long way off. Or is it?

While the idea of artificial intelligence (AI) goes back to the mid-50s, Isaac Asimov was writing about robot intelligence in 1942 (the word 'robot' comes from a Czech word often translated as 'drudgery'). A generally accepted test for artificial machine intelligence, the Turing test, also dates back to the 1950s, when the British mathematician Alan Turing suggested that we would have AI when it was possible for someone to talk to a machine without realizing it was a machine.

The Turing test is problematic on some levels, though. First, a small child is generally intelligent, but most would probably fail the test. Second, if something artificial were to develop consciousness, why would it automatically let us know? Perhaps it would keep this to itself and refuse to participate in childish intelligence tests.

The 60s and 70s saw a great deal of progress in AI, but breakthroughs failed to come. Instead scientists and developers focused on specific problems, such as speech and text recognition and computer vision. However, we may now be less than a decade away from seeing the AI vision become a reality.

timeline

1990	**2011**	**2027**	**2040**
iRobot Corporation founded to manufacture industrial and domestic robots	Watson, an IBM computer, wins *Jeopardy!*, a US TV show	A $79 toaster passes the Turing test	$750 smartphone contains as much processing power as a human brain

AI on the way In 2008 a personal computer was able to handle around 10 billion instructions per second. Sounds a lot. But that's roughly the same as the brain of a small fish. By around 2040 machine brains should, in theory, be able to handle around 100 trillion instructions per second. That's about the same as a human brain. So what happens when machine intelligence starts to rival that of its human designers?

Before we descend down this rabbit hole we should first split AI in two. 'Strong AI' is the term generally used to describe true thinking machines. 'Weak AI' (sometimes known as 'Narrow AI') is intelligence intended to supplement rather than exceed human intelligence. So far most machines are preprogrammed or taught logical courses of action. But in the future, machines with strong AI will be able to learn as they go and respond to unexpected events. The implications? Think of automated disease diagnosis and surgery, military planning and battle command, customer-service avatars, artificial creativity and autonomous robots that predict then respond to crime (a 'Department of Future Crime' – see also pages 86 and 103).

Are these examples realistic? Some experts might say yes. Ray Kurzweil, an American futurist and inventor, has made a public bet with Mitchell Kapor, the founder of Lotus software, that a computer will pass the Turing test by 2029. Other experts say no. Bill Calvin, an American theoretical neurophysiologist, suggests the human brain is so 'buggy' that computers

> ❝The main lesson of 35 years of AI research is that the hard problems are easy and the easy problems are hard. The mental abilities of a four-year-old that we take for granted ... in fact, solve some of the hardest engineering problems ever conceived.❞
>
> **Steven Pinker,** psychologist, cognitive scientist and author

2042	**2050**	**2054**	**2069**
Software virus disables 90 per cent of machines	Intelligent robots outnumber human beings	Machines start to paint and compose music	Machines demand equal rights

> **❝I am putting myself to the fullest possible use, which is all I think that any conscious entity can ever hope to do.❞**
>
> **HAL, the computer in**
> **2001: A Space Odyssey (1968)**

will never be able to emulate it or, if they do, machines will inherit our foibles and emotional inadequacies along with our intelligence. Think of the computer called HAL in the film *2001: A Space Odyssey*.

But perhaps we are all looking in the wrong direction. The Internet is already fostering an unanticipated form of self-organizing chaos: a highly efficient marketplace for ideas, reputations and information known as collective intelligence, from which AI may emerge. Adam Smith suggested that buyers and sellers, each pursuing his own interest, would together produce more goods, more efficiently, than under any other arrangement. The same is happening with online suppliers and potentially with customers too. Wikipedia, for instance, can create more knowledge, with less bias and over a wider span of disciplines, than any group of experts ever could.

What next?   There is little doubt that AI will progress significantly in the years ahead. Some commentators say that where AI is now similar to where personal computing was in around 2004, so progress could be astonishing. Historically, our approach to AI has been brute force, but once parallel computing techniques become established (quantum or DNA computing, for instance – see Chapter 17) true AI could be achieved very rapidly.

The Chinese room experiment

In 1980, John Searle, an American philosopher, argued in a paper that a computer, or perhaps more accurately a bit of software, could pass the Turing test and behave much like a human being at a distance without being truly intelligent – that words, symbols or instructions could be interpreted or reacted to without any true understanding. In what has become known as the Chinese room thought experiment (because of the use of Chinese characters to interact with an unknown person – actually a computer), Searle argued that it's perfectly possible for a computer to simulate the illusion of intelligence, or give the illusion of understanding a human being, without really doing so.

Self-driving cars

Gone are the days when Google was just a search engine and cars needed a driver. Google's autonomous car project, started by Sebastian Thrun of Stanford Artificial Intelligence Laboratory, uses a Toyota Prius equipped with sensors to follow a GPS route all by itself. A robotics scientist sits in the car, but doesn't actually drive it. Already, seven cars have travelled 1,600km (1,000 miles) with no driver and 225,000km (140,000 miles) with occasional human intervention.

Nevertheless, two big questions remain. First, is the human brain essentially just a machine with a bunch of wiring and some chemistry and electricity thrown in, or is there much more to it than that? If the human brain is simply a collection of atoms, then surely it can be only a matter of time before we design machines that can match and possibly exceed human capabilities. If this happens, we are presumably on the cusp of a new era of human evolution where we start to merge with our machines and gain a level of immortality. Indeed, perhaps this exists already in the sense that the 'real' us is our DNA, and our bodies are merely temporary packages to carry it around. Second, even if machines do not reach this level of sophistication, it's likely that they'll become very smart indeed, so what happens to the people who previously did the things that machines will do in the future?

Welcome to the future. It's metallic and uses lots of batteries. Hopefully, it's not angry and it won't work out a way to enslave the human race.

the condensed idea
The machines wake up

21 Personalized genomics

It's now possible to sequence, then analyse, the genome of individuals to predict specific human traits or to forecast the probability that an individual will suffer from certain conditions or diseases. To do this used to cost millions. In the future it'll be almost nothing.

A genome is basically genetic information, or instructions, embedded either as DNA, RNA, or proteins. These three types of molecule can be found in all known life forms. If you can access some of this information you can make fairly accurate guesstimates about the future – specifically, individual predispositions to some types of disease or adverse reactions to certain drugs.

All you will have to do is provide a tiny bit of saliva, post it together with a fistful of dollars (or pounds) and you can find out almost everything you need to know. You can track distant ancestry, susceptibility to different types of disease, and determine, with a reasonable level of accuracy, dispositions to alcoholism, cocaine addiction and possibly depression. Give it a decade, perhaps two, and this test might be available free, via your hospital or private health-insurance company.

Access all areas What is perhaps most amazing about this is the fact that the cost of generating sequence data has dropped much faster than the cost of computing. Moore's Law is frequently quoted to demonstrate the accelerating effects of technology (see Chapter 17), but genomic sequencing is outperforming computing power in this respect.

timeline

1997	2008	2009	2012
Release of the movie *Gattaca* about genetic enhancement	Knome offers genome sequencing to individuals for $350,000	Knome drops its price to $99,500	23andMe offers gene sequencing for $299

Retail genomics

Named after the fact that everyone has 23 pairs of chromosomes, 23andMe is a private Californian company that allows ordinary individuals to find out about and understand their personal genomics. The fact that the company is backed financially by Google might seem rather odd to some people, but if Google's aim is to organize the world's information, they will clearly need everyone's DNA. Products available from 23andMe include ancestry testing and healthcare screening, especially with regard to how an individual's genes might impact on their future health and healthcare costs.

Yet in both cases, our ability to create information may soon outstrip our ability to store and especially analyse it. Nevertheless, personalized genome sequencing will help to usher in a new era in which medicine is increasingly tailored to an individual.

The Google-backed biotech company 23andMe was offering individuals gene sequencing for $999 in 2011. At the time of writing (June 2012) the cost had fallen to $299. A decade earlier this would have cost close to $10,000, while James Watson, the co-discoverer of DNA and one of the people behind the Human Genome Project, paid around $2 billion to work out how to make sequencing work. Interestingly, 23andMe plugs into the idea of crowd-sourcing data, too, by sending regular questionnaires to thousands of users asking about them about, for example, specific food allergies. When the responses to such surveys are matched against known genetic information they can

> **A person is not an originating agent; he is a locus, a point at which many genetic and environmental conditions come together in a joint effect.**
>
> **B.F. Skinner,** psychologist, inventor and author

2018	2020	2030	2050
Cost falls to $49 via Walmart	Hospitals and insurers offer free genome profiling	Google dating based upon ideal DNA profiles	DNA database creates human underclass

Biocriminology

Crime has always fascinated people – and the reasons why criminals commit crimes, even more so. Now the field of biocriminology – which uses new techniques such as brain imaging and neuroendocrinology to predict disposition to commit crimes – is starting to threaten the strongholds of criminology. Biocriminology posits that people's genes or hormones predispose them towards criminal behaviour. This upsets traditional criminologists, who believe that environment, particularly poverty, is a more credible reason. There are currently fewer than two dozen people publishing biocriminology articles, in part because the traditional outlets are so wary about them, but also because these studies still lack the required rigour. It's challenging to identify more than links between biology and behaviour because of the difficulty of separating them from environmental variables, such as drugs and alcohol or poor diet. Expect the controversy to develop rapidly alongside our knowledge of the workings of the human brain.

potentially find the causes of certain traits in a matter of months rather than years and for minimal cost.

Power to the patient What are the main outcomes of being able to access this type of information? For one thing, more accurate diagnosis of common conditions. It also opens the way for individuals to be prescribed certain drugs or to be warned against certain known risk factors or environments associated with particular conditions. For instance, if you know you have a genetic disposition to high blood pressure you may be persuaded to eat more healthy foods and take more exercise. Thus medicine shifts away from cure to prediction and prevention. If we develop a better understanding of how genes act, this also means that we will be able to target individuals suffering from a certain illness with one type of drug rather than another. In other words, testing can identify not whether you have a condition *right now* but the probability that you will, in *the future*, develop a problem for which you'll need to be screened on a regular basis.

Linked to personalized genome sequencing is the emerging field of biomarkers. This is where a molecule is created that is combined with a marking agent, which then attaches itself to, for instance, a known tumour type. Advanced imaging technology can then be used to track the presence and development of such tumours. There is even the future possibility of attaching a serum to these biomarkers that will effectively 'turn off' any tumours if they are found. Whether this will work or not is anyone's guess. Perhaps we'll become obsessed with predicting the future – mentally and physically – and those that can will pay to offset the risks. Or we may all become fatalistic and just carry on as though this knowledge doesn't exist. People still smoke, after all.

> **We are at the beginning of a personal-genomics revolution that will transform not only how we take care of ourselves but also what we mean by personal information.**
>
> *Time* magazine, 2008

While personalized genomic sequencing promises great things, the reality will almost certainly prove to be far more complex and confusing than the theory. For instance, the interplay between hidden hereditary factors and random external forces (where we live, what we do for a living, diet, exercise and so on) is horribly confusing. Nevertheless, expect to see a plethora of quick tests and tiny devices in the future that will diagnose everything from the probability that you will suffer from certain medical problems to estimates of your likely life span. These will be based on various genetic factors overlaid, perhaps, with personalized and real-time information about where you've been, what you've eaten and the amount of exercise you've taken – gleaned from various sources ranging from mobile phones that capture geographic locations and retail payments to running shoes and clothes that measure movement and distances travelled.

the condensed idea
Genetic prophesy

22 Regenerative medicine

Is it possible to prevent or reverse the ageing process, perhaps by fiddling with tired tissues and cells, or even growing new organs inside a laboratory? Some people regard this as a pipe dream. Others see it instead as increasingly inevitable.

Physician, heal thyself. What if you are an ageing surgeon and parts of your body are worn out? Options may include stem-cell therapy, the transplant of an artificial organ (a kidney grown *in vitro*), the printing of replacement teeth or bones using a fabricator, general life extension, some more hair, or perhaps some new fingers? This last idea may seem a little far-fetched, but if newts can repair themselves why not human beings? One way to do so might be to persuade cells to return to a younger state – in other words, trick the body into believing that it's a young child once again. This sounds incredible, but there's a serious possibility that by the end of this century, and possibly a lot sooner, human beings will be able to regrow lost limbs.

> **❝I think that given sufficient funding we have a 50/50 chance of completely stopping people from dying of old age within about 25 or 30 years from now.❞**
>
> **Aubrey de Grey,** gerontology theoretician and author

Our ageing population As we've already seen, the growth in the world's population over the past 100 years or so has not been caused by people having lots of sex, but the fact that we haven't been dying as young or as frequently as we used to. In other words, population growth is intimately linked with healthcare and associated areas such as diet and lifestyle.

timeline

2010	2025	2030	2032
Bionic ears widely available	Tooth regeneration creates unemployment among dentists	Organs grown from stem cells available on eBay	1.2 billion people aged 65+

So the world is now full of lots of older people. One consequence of ageing in prosperous populations is that more people want to put off the inevitable. In short, people don't want to die *at all* and many have the means to ensure that, while they may not achieve immortality, they can certainly reach a ripe old age. Add some future scientific breakthroughs and technological marvels and you have a smorgasbord of options to extend both the quality and quantity of an individual's life. For instance, in 2011 a patient was given a new windpipe grown in a laboratory using the patient's own cells. Growing skin, pipes, blood vessels, bladders and even stomachs is either happening already or is not far off. Whether we can eventually grow solid organs such as hearts, kidneys and lungs raises more complex issues, but it's not impossible.

But things could go much further. Human life spans have grown from 45 years for men and 49 for women in 1901 in the UK to 76 and 81

Young blood

Research by Thomas Rando at Stamford University suggests that older people might recover from injuries faster if they were given drugs developed from the blood of young people. In an experiment, pairs of mice were joined together to create artificially conjoined twins. The result was that old mice who were connected to young mice regenerated muscle cells much faster than pairs of old mice. Apparently, the effect has nothing to do with stems cells contained in the young blood either. This suggests that older bodies repair themselves more slowly because of a lack of some signal or other – not because the stem cells lose their regenerative ability. This finding is likely to result in various 'fast repair' products for older people in the future.

2033	2035	2038	2043
Global life expectancy now 80 years	Alzheimer's disease is finally cured	Robots carry out 80 per cent of operations	Treatment allows amputees to regrow lost limbs

❛The stroke of death is as a lover's pinch, which hurts and is desired.❜
William Shakespeare, poet and playwright

respectively in 2002. So why can't this extension be repeated over the next 100 years? Why can't nature and nurture be tweaked to extend life spans even further? The current record is 122 years, but why can't this be 150? Indeed, why can't we kill off the very idea of death itself? Again, you're probably thinking that this is crazy. After all, surely all life broadly follows the second law of thermodynamics, which states that decay is inevitable?

What's possible? In the more optimistic corner, are those who believe that ageing is genetically determined and that the 'death programme' or process that causes ageing can be switched off, or at least amended. Aubrey de Grey, editor of *Rejuvenation* magazine and co-founder of rejuvenation research organization the SENS Foundation, has even suggested that there is no scientific reason why human beings cannot live to 1,000. He has even suggested that this person may even be alive right now.

On the face of it, this is a very exciting idea. Around 90 per cent of deaths worldwide are caused by ageing so imagine what would happen if you could slow death down or eradicate it. But there are moral and even philosophical issues here. The first issue is practical. If we 'solved' death, there would be many more mouths to feed on the planet. Perhaps we can solve this technologically. But if it were common to live to 110, 130 or 150, people might wait until they were 60, 70 or even 80 to have children.

Significantly extended life spans could also wreak havoc on marriage with 'until death do us part' taking on a whole new meaning. And there remains the problem that death is to some extent useful in that it creates space – in the sense of mentally rather than physically – for new people with new ideas. Death, in part, is what moves the world forward.

It isn't just about our physical bodies. Our minds age too and many people have just had enough life by the time they reach their 70s, 80s and 90s. According to Dignitas (a Swiss organization that helps people to die at a

Future treatments

Stem-cell medicine promises two radical future developments. The first is a series of treatments for diseases such as Alzheimer's and Parkinson's disease. The second is the production of genetically matching organs (farmed or printed using 3D fabricators) to replace those damaged by normal ageing or disease, or by treatments for illness, for example, a liver damaged during cancer treatment. Historically, stem cells have been a difficult ethical area, because the process of stem-cell production for the most useful stem cells involved the destruction of human embryos. But this isn't necessarily true for new techniques, such as the iPS cell developed at Kyoto University, which means that the area is likely to grow rapidly.

time and place of their own choosing), 21 per cent of the people who come to them have nothing wrong with them. They are simply tired of life.

The pros and cons of immortality is a complex debate, but it's not one we'll be having for a while. In the meantime, many of us can just enjoy ourselves and look forward to a much longer and healthier life. But be careful. According to the *British Journal of Sports Medicine*, every 60 minutes someone spends watching TV after the age of 25 reduces life expectancy by an average of 21.8 minutes. So be mindful of how you choose to spend your time and perhaps congratulate yourself on the fact that you're reading this rather than watching yet another rerun of *Friends* on TV.

the condensed idea
Alive for longer

23 Remote monitoring

Imagine a bandage that not only protected your wound, but could talk to your doctor about it, a bandage that could transmit information about changes in your body temperature, heart rate, blood pressure, glucose levels or breathing. Medical records would, of course, be updated instantly to the cloud.

From a patient's point of view, ideas such as 'talkative' wound dressings are attractive because they are non-intrusive, painless and highly convenient. Patients can still get out of bed, move about independently, and even reduce the length of time they're in hospital. For people with chronic diseases, such as diabetes or heart disease, remote monitoring (sometimes known as telemedicine, which is related to self-tracking and what is sometimes referred to as e-health) could even help to keep them away from hospital unless absolutely necessary.

All of this already exists and it's a fast-growing field – but the future possibilities are almost endless. Consider, for example, what other conditions might be monitored with such bandages: alcohol levels, for example, or signs of excess anxiety before panic attacks. Or how about epidermal electronics (e.g. press-on tattoos) enabling constant medical monitoring for depression or suicide?

Home monitoring Some experts are already advocating at-home monitoring of patients, saving travel time and inconvenience, while putting a lid on the spiralling healthcare costs associated with common

timeline

2012
Kettles in Japan that monitor health of elderly living alone

2014
Relaunch of Google Health

2030
All kitchen and bathroom appliances allow linkage to GPs and hospitals

2032
Computers implanted in 20 per cent of human beings

chips with everything

How likely is it that we will have microchips implanted in our bodies in the future? A British computer scientist called Robin Warwick implanted an RFID chip (see page 5) in his body to do various routine tasks such as opening doors and turning on lights in 1998. The idea obviously has some ethical implications, and privacy and data theft are also serious issues. But what if, in the future, legislation is passed that gives every individual a unique email or communications address, and details of this address, together with bank details and medical records, are added to the chip too? Indeed, it's not too far-fetched to imagine a future world where all commercial transactions and online communications require identity authorization, provided by internal chips – and it's illegal to have these authorized chips tampered with or removed.

conditions. Analysts estimate that the market for home medical monitoring for chronic conditions will soon be worth billions, especially with elderly populations set to explode in most regions. There are other advantages to home-based monitoring, too. For example, an ability to diagnose patients in very remote locations. Even better, how about actually conducting surgery via robotics when the patient is in one place and the surgeon (possibly a robot) is in another? This is something else that's already happening and has huge potential, especially in developing regions.

As for treatments that are actually implanted inside the human body, we have already seen implantable brain devices to treat depression and Parkinson's disease, implantable defibrillators to treat early-stage heart attacks and implantable glucose monitors to keep an eye on sugar levels and insulin delivery. What's up next includes: bone-growing implants

2035

Hackers target individually implanted life-support systems

2040

Implantable devices give early warnings of depression and suicide

2050

All clothing items contain sensors to monitor health in real time

Very remote medicine

One advantage of using telecommunications in medicine is the ability to treat people in remote locations. An extreme example of this was in 2001, when a surgeon in New York removed the gall bladder of a patient in Paris using robotic surgery. But true advances in telemedicine will move towards prevention rather than cure, and will be able to monitor people before they get sick. For example, BodyTel, in Germany, measures glucose levels, blood pressure and weight using wireless technology. The American company Honeywell gives patients similar abilities to monitor ECG, oxygen levels and blood pressure, while doctors continually review the data.

(to stimulate cells into repairing damaged or regrowing missing bone), devices to suppress hunger (electrical trickery to make the stomach think it's full even when it's not), remote-controlled insulin pumps and defibrillators, migraine neutralizers and next-generation brain implants to control drug-resistant depression.

For patients who cannot monitor themselves, e.g. Alzheimer's patients, there are technologies coming to do it for them. For example, a smart walking stick can calculate the gait of the patient after, say, a hip replacement. Or sensors around the home, on pill boxes, kettles or baths, can tell carers what's going on when they're not around. There may even come a time when well people wear sensors that will act as an early-warning system for diseases. Most likely, mobile phones will offer medical monitoring in the future, too. If diseases are detected at early stages, they are cheaper to treat and have less impact on the patient and on medical budgets. On the other hand, if sensors are constantly detecting symptoms in a population, there will be reams of data to analyse and doctors will be under constant pressure to attend to data, rather than to people.

This means programming computers to analyse the data *before* alerting a doctor, so in the future, the doctor will call the patient, rather than the patient calling them. Linked with ideas like these are a host of others ranging from online tools to help facilitate a second opinion on medical bills to online menu pricing for elective surgery or even online reservation systems for doctors' appointments.

Internal medicine Not futuristic enough for you? How about microrobots, or other tiny devices, for the observation and delivery of drugs and surgery deep inside the body? A few years ago, a research team placed a tiny robot inside a test tube full of water and manipulated it with a joystick to grab hold of yeast cells (15 microns in size). A 1cm movement with the joystick created a 1 micron movement of the robot, with a force of one-10 billionth of a gram that the researchers felt amplified 500 billion-fold in the joystick.

It is startling to imagine how this technique of 'swallowing the surgeon' could develop. Olympus Medical Systems Corp has invented capsule endoscopy, where the miniature endoscope can be swallowed and provides information as it travels down the gastrointestinal tract (GIT). It is already being used in 300 hospitals in Japan. The only problem with these capsules? They are easy to swallow and excrete via the GIT, but how could devices such as microbots be removed from the circulatory system, for example, after injecting them? These are the kinds of questions that researchers will need to address over coming decades.

Remote monitoring is a good thing. For instance, it allows elderly people to stay in their own homes for longer. But there's the possibility that it will create further isolation. There's the danger that society will see this as a way of sending 'them' off elsewhere. But 'them' is 'us' in time and what we all need, especially when we get older, is people. We need to know that we are not alone, and machines, even e-plasters, cannot do this.

> **❛The doctor of the future will give no medicine, but will interest his patients in the care of the human frame, in diet and in the cause and prevention of disease.❜**
>
> **Thomas Edison, inventor**

the condensed idea
24/7 medical monitoring

24 User-generated medicine

If you thought user-generated and user-filtered material was limited to media and entertainment, you'd be wrong. Medicine has recently seen an outbreak of cancer videos, wellness wikis and bulimia blogs, all of which represent the early stages of a shift in the balance of power towards the end-user or patient.

Online support groups have been around for years and the distribution of material related to specific medical conditions via physical meetings has been around even longer, for example, within the HIV/Aids community, but increasing connectivity now allows patients to find other people suffering from similar conditions instantly and allows them to talk to each other about treatments. The website patientslikeme.com, which features 150,000-plus patients suffering from over 1,000 medical conditions, is a good example of how this is developing.

Health 2.0 The popularity of Web 2.0, or user-generated sites, such as YouTube, Facebook, Flickr and Wikipedia, have made the creation and filtering of information easier and more immediate and it's easy to see why some people are getting so excited about the prospects for 'Health 2.0', e-health and user-generated medical content. It allows patients to control their own destiny and represents a significant shift in power away from the medical profession and pharmaceuticals industry towards the individual patient. One issue, for example, is why some medical records still held by medical institutions are often on paper. This is slowly changing, but until we achieve a shift in attitudes relating to who has access to what

timeline

2014
Apple introduce iMedic monitoring feature on iPhone 6

2018
Dunnhumby and Tesco put in charge of 25 per cent of UK hospitals

2020
Launch of Medipedia, a crowd-sourced medical directory

and in what format, this will act against not only the generation and transmission of knowledge by small groups of patients, but will also prevent the occurrence of larger network effects (i.e 'the wisdom of crowds').

But does user-generated medicine or 'open-source health' really have a future? On the one hand, you'd think that privacy issues alone would prevent any meaningful exchange of knowledge, but this doesn't seem to be an issue. Equally, you might suspect that the information itself would be unreliable, or even harmful, but a study in the *British Medical Journal* found that just 6 per cent of such information was factually inaccurate. According to Jupiter Research, 70 per cent of US Internet users have now generated some kind

> **'This artificial distinction between a consumer and a producer is dissolving, I call it the participant economy. Web 2.0 is about people.'**
>
> David Sifry, Technorati

Joined-up medicine

User-generated and user-filtered content is a defining feature of social media, so why not apply the same tools and techniques to medicine? The argument against so doing is that medicine can be a matter of life and death and is best left to experts. The argument in favour of user-generated medicine is that experts cannot possibly know everything or keep up with every latest development across all areas of health, and that sometimes patients really do know what's best for them. Perhaps the best way forward is a combination of both. Leave diagnosis and treatment of serious medical conditions to the professionals, but encourage patients to talk to each other and allow them to form specialist networks where drugs and treatment results can be compared.

2025	2030	2040
All medical records accessed via the 'cloud'	All hospitals rated eBay style by patients	TripAdvisor launches hospital review spin-off

'Medicine is the only profession that labours incessantly to destroy the reason for its own existence.'

James Bryce, politician and diplomat

of online health-related information and, according to a PEW Internet & American Life study, almost a third of Americans who have used the Web to find medical information say that the information has been beneficial.

Connecting patients In the future, people will post their genetic profiles online as openly as they currently post photographs and descriptions of their lives on Facebook. Indeed, if the early history of the Web teaches us anything, it's that the killer application of the Internet is connecting people together and that we will share many of our innermost secrets, including life-and-death information, about our minds and bodies.

We'll be logging onto genealogy sites to find out where we've come from and using predictive software to work out where our offspring will be going in the future if harry630@mappleymail ends up with sally330@zlingee. These genetic networks will open up a host of privacy issues, not only for us but also for our parents and grandparents too. And you can be sure that everyone from governments and hospitals to insurance companies and even the police will be pretty keen to see what's hidden inside our bodies once the data goes public. Such information will undoubtedly spawn a flood of quackery and self-prescribed medicine, but networked patients and treatment networks also offer the possibility of open medical innovation. Currently, drug companies and regulatory agencies shy away from certain ideas, but if the freedom to experiment passes to the wisdom of the crowd we may see a blossoming of new possibilities.

In essence, what user-generated medicine means is more people taking personal responsibility for their health. The old days of consulting the doctor when you have a problem are gone. Everything now is based on your lifestyle and your choices (and perhaps your salary or your private medical insurance). These days nobody's an expert. And if they are, you probably can't afford them.

The drugs don't work

Roughly 90 per cent of drugs don't work for 30–50 per cent of people, so it's perhaps no surprise that drug companies are moving away from the blockbuster business model towards more personalized treatments. The reasons for this are two-fold. First, many drugs are starting to fall out of patent restrictions, and generic drug makers (particularly in Asia) are becoming more aggressive about attacking patents so that generic 'lookalike' drugs are getting to be cheaper and more commonplace. The second reason for the trend is technology. Developments in areas such as genomics and personal phenotyping mean that personalized medicine is becoming a reality, and pharmaceutical companies are shifting research and development expenditure towards speciality products and therapies that target niche medical conditions and subpopulations. A 9 million euro, EU-funded project, Food4Me, is being launched to look at all aspects of personalized nutrition – namely how food intake could be tailored to suit each individual's physical and genetic make-up.

Perhaps rather than call it personalized medicine, we should call it personalized health. There's even a European study on delivering personalized nutrition according to phenotype. In the end, it really is up to you to look after yourself by whatever method you choose from the hundreds of possibilities available so that you don't need medicine. Yes, patients know best and can be trusted to have access to all their data.

the condensed idea
Patient power

25 Medical data mining

Medicine, like insurance, isn't always that smart. Both tend to be reactive, and personal risks are assessed using aggregated historical data, which is linked to questions about how old someone is, where they live and what they do for a living. But growing debts, together with demands placed on healthcare by societal ageing and developments in digital technology, mean this method won't last for long.

Supermarkets, coffee shops and pizza parlours have long used precision marketing – for example, sophisticated social segmentation techniques – to help them decide where to build stores in order to achieve maximum sales. Now heath planners are starting to target those local communities most in need of testing or intervention using the same technique. Of course, ironically, many of the medical conditions that medical planners hope to target are precisely the ones that places such as pizza joints are creating in the first place. For retailers, data-mining techniques are intended to maximize customer spend. With healthcare the idea is to use similar data to reduce costs.

For example, diabetes, largely caused by sedentary lifestyles and people eating too much unhealthy food, is a global epidemic in the making. Worldwide there are 285 million people with diabetes and in the USA diabetes rates have doubled since 1980.

By 2030, 438 million people will be diagnosed with diabetes according to the International Diabetes Federation – a staggering 7.8 per cent of the

timeline

1870	1921	1928	1985
Germ theory of disease formulated	Insulin developed	Penicillin discovered	Surgical robot conducts first operation

Hidden digital data trails

One of the key issues we'll have to debate in the future is what to do with the vast amounts of new data that will be generated at both a micro and macro level. Much of the new data connected to where individuals are and what they're doing will be hugely useful to governments and corporations alike, so who owns the data and how it's protected will be hugely contentious. We should expect data crime to increase significantly, not just at an intergovernmental cyber-crime level, but also at a corporate espionage or intellectual property level too. As for ordinary individuals, it's possible that the default setting will be 'public' and that individuals will have to pay to keep their own data private and confidential.

world's adult population. The cost of dealing with this is immense – $418 billion in 2010. North America alone spends $214 billion treating the disease, and if you project the costs forward a decade or two, treatments could become unaffordable unless something dramatic is done. But there is hope. About 5 per cent of the US population consumes about 50 per cent of all US healthcare spending, and if you could find these people sooner rather than later, you would reduce treatment costs substantially.

> **❝It's funny how all living organisms are alike ... when the chips are down, when the pressure is on, every creature on the face of the Earth is interested in one thing and one thing only. Its own survival.❞**
> **Dr Iris Hineman,** in the film *Minority Report* (2002)

2001	2008	2020	2030
Telesurgery performed	Almost full-face transplant carried out	Healthcare rationing linked to lifestyle choices	Medical data hacking becomes an epidemic

Where data mining comes in Using sophisticated research and segmentation techniques, data mining can be used to target people living on specific streets or attending certain schools or workplaces. For example, a campaign in Slough (UK) targeted individuals most in need of screening for Type 2 diabetes. Of the 2,000 people identified using social categorization, 106 were discovered to be undiagnosed Type 2 sufferers. A similar campaign in Brent (UK) targeted teenage pregnancy.

Add to this molecular diagnostics, genetic screening and the use of markers, and doctors will be able to detect diseases earlier and, in some cases, before they occur, which will reduce treatment costs and increase survival rates. Link all this to new imaging technologies, remote monitoring, medical smartcards, e-records and even gamification. One day, we may, for example, develop a tiny chip that can hold the full medical history of a person including any medical conditions, allergies, prescriptions and contact information (this is already planned in America).

The card could feature a picture ID and hours of video content, such as X-rays or moving medical imagery. Synchronize this with digital payment systems (the contents of your wallet will have been put inside your phone or inside the same implanted chip by this time) and you end up with exhaustive historical and real-time data about where people are and how they live. This can then be used to predict how they might die unless some kind of intervention takes place.

Digital vacuums

Digital vacuuming refers to the practice of scooping up vast amounts of data then using mathematical and statistical models to determine content and possible linkages. The data itself can be anything from phone calls in historical or real time (the US company AT&T, for example, holds the records of 1.9 trillion telephone calls) to financial transactions, emails and Internet site visits. Commercial applications could include future health risks to counter-terrorism.

> **I shall go further and say that even if an examination of the past could lead to any valid prediction concerning man's future, that prediction would be the contrary of reassuring.**
>
> **Julien Benda, philosopher**

Looking to the future However, while such ideas could prove effective, what's the cost in terms of privacy? For example, health services targeting people that aren't yet ill, but whose profile suggests that they will be in the future, is spookily reminiscent of the Department of Future Crimes or Precrime in the film *Minority Report*. Or what if a 'Department of Future Health' found through data analysis and e-records that alcoholism or lung cancer was a specific problem in one community. In such cases, should the government act to remove products such as alcohol and tobacco from shops in the area? If you're thinking that this could never happen in Europe or the USA, in Australia the sale of alcohol is already banned in certain Aboriginal communities.

One further example of the shape of things to come is something called the Heritage Provider Network (HPN). HPN are seeking to develop an algorithm to prevent the unnecessary hospitalization of patients – identified as a $30 billion problem in the USA back in 2006. The network, whose website is heritagehealthprize.com, is offering a series of milestone prizes of $230,000 and a grand prize totalling $3 million to any individual or institution that can develop a way of predicting the number of days patients will spend in hospital.

the condensed idea
A Department of Future Sickness

26 Living alone

Across the world, the family unit is changing. The nuclear family consisting of mum, dad and two kids is disappearing. In its place we're seeing various family blends emerge. Indeed, the traditional family unit is becoming less traditional. However, the key trend isn't families at all, but people living by themselves. Around 34 per cent of people in the UK live alone.

In the future, more people will be living alone or with platonic flatmates outside traditional married relationships. While many house-sharers are likely to be young professionals, others may be elderly friends, sharing for safety, companionship and cost. Those who do live with their families could be part of a multigenerational cohabitation trend. Think of grandparents moving in to help with childcare or older kids not leaving home, to save money.

Historically, people generally lived on their own because they were young, widowed or divorced. It was usually a temporary state and all manner of events were created to bring people together. Not any more. For many people, singledom is now the preferred state. But what does it say about a society when we can't be bothered to engage meaningfully with another person? Is it a sign of narcissism, laziness, perfectionism, individualism or simply that people don't have the time to invest in a career and a relationship? Perhaps digitalization and virtualization have removed the need for physical presence.

Figures released by the UK Office for National Statistics show that married women are now in a minority in England and Wales. One of the main

timeline

2014	2015	2016	2017
40 per cent of British adults live alone	Tax benefits for grandparents living with grandchildren	Walmart discontinues 'family packs' in USA	Banks offer 100-year cross-generational mortgages

reasons is that women are delaying marriage until their 30s and 40s. In the early 1970s, for example, around 85 per cent of women were married by the time they were 30. Now the figure is less than 33 per cent. Other reasons are that divorce has become easier and women are outliving their husbands.

> **'Loneliness is the ultimate poverty.'**
> **Abigail Van Buren,**
> **advice columnist**

Changing boundaries The emotional and financial consequences of this are significant and will certainly impact on future government policy. By 2038, for instance, the number of UK couples who live together, but are not married, is projected to double from 2 million to almost 4 million, so the legal strength of relationships may become more fragile. This will almost certainly have a negative effect on children, but there are likely to be fewer children in the future too due to a mixture of cost and careers. Also, if family size shrinks and governments become more indebted, who will look after our old?

Singled out

A survey by Duke University has found that single men and women with heart disease who lack close friends are more than 300 per cent more likely to die within five years than those who are married or have a close networks of friends. Another study, from Yale, has found that men and women who said they were loved had significantly less blockages in their coronary arteries than those who said they were not. In other words, love and intimacy (or the lack of it) are among the most fundamental causes of what makes us sick or well. For example, when people are feeling lonely, depressed or emotionally anxious they may take refuge in food, alcohol and drugs, which can in turn lead to sickness and premature death. This in turn raises the question of whether a society that encourages individualism is literally killing us.

2018	**2019**	**2024**	**2026**
60 per cent of 30-year-olds still living at home	Social networks start to establish physical communities	Social robots in 30 per cent of single-person households	People living alone own 90 per cent of all pets in China

> **You have brains in your head. You have feet in your shoes. You can steer yourself in any direction you choose. You're on your own. And you know what you know. You are the guy who'll decide where to go.**
>
> **Dr Seuss,** writer and cartoonist

We are potentially creating a society where many more people live alone, but the social-support structures to look after people when they are old or sick wither.

In the USA it's much the same story. It seems that Americans aren't getting married as much as they used to either, or at least married couples aren't as common, which again could have significant repercussions for government policy-making. However, despite the decline of the traditional American household, it seems that the desire to be part of some kind of couple is as strong as ever, even if you don't actually live together. Moreover, the figures highlight the trend for delaying marriage rather than signalling its total disappearance. We should not forget that communities do not always have to be physical either, as the many online communities testify.

Another trend: since property is now so expensive, cohabiting has become a more economical and convenient option for many singles. Cohabitation is seen by many individuals as a test-drive (test-bed?) for legal marriage. Maybe what we'll see in the future is people living together for pre-agreed time periods (or child-raising contracts), with couples committed to raising children for 20 or 25 years before reverting to singledom, either due to a desire for freedom or to pursue another relationship. People may also split then cohabit with friends or colleagues to increase security or to save money.

Single-person future So what are some of the other implications of a world where more people live on their own? One area affected is retail. Increased numbers of single-person households, especially in inner-city areas, mean that value and convenience are usually more important than choice. One mundane, but nevertheless prophetic, example is that items such as chicken breasts can now be bought in packs of one in urban supermarkets rather than just in packs of two, four or six. This could be a profitable area for retailers because the margins on single-serve packs are often greater than on larger packs. Another is collaborative consumption, where people share resources because it's cheaper than each individual owning, say, a car.

It's only me

In a supermarket, nobody can hear you scream: 'I'm all alone.' Indeed, for now the world is still largely prepackaged for couples and families. Steaks often come in packs of two and four, restaurant tables are meant for two, four, six and eight, and cars are made for two, three, four, five or more. Of course, there are some advantages to living alone. The dustbins don't fill up as fast and there's always enough hot water for a bath. But is living alone healthy for the planet? In the future, people who live alone might have to pay higher taxes, because doing so means more housing, household appliances and cars. Or will they find new ways of sharing resources through collaborative consumption?

Another implication may be health. A Danish study found that older people who live alone have a greater risk of a sudden heart episode than those living with others. It's a danger for men over 50, but not so much for women until they hit 60; but for both sexes, living alone after this age can double the risk of a heart episode. The authors note that it's important to look beyond physical factors such as diabetes and smoking and examine the social and environmental issues that may contribute to heart disease. This ties in with previous studies which suggest that those of a lower socio-economic group or with a lack of social support are a higher risk group for trouble. While social isolation may play a big part in this, people who live alone have an increased likelihood of classic individual risk factors such as smoking, obesity and a high-cholesterol diet.

the condensed idea
More people living alone

27 Dematerialization

The global economy is becoming dematerialized. What this means is that many things that have, or create, value no longer exist in a physical domain. The currency of this new economy is still money, but it's digital money generated by ideas and information. Furthermore, this shift from physical manufacturing to digital services and virtual experiences has barely begun.

Digitalization represents a significant shift in terms of how things are made, and it's changing how, where and what people consume. For example, the old industrial-age model required large inputs of capital and labour to create value. Inputs tended to be relatively expensive and barriers to market entry were high. As a result, growth rates tended to be relatively modest and innovation tended to be slow. This is still partly true, in some instances, but physical inputs, both in terms of capital and labour, are declining significantly. Indeed, with increasing automation we are, in a sense, getting to a point where capital actually becomes labour.

Physical goods, where they do still exist, are becoming much smaller and lighter, requiring fewer materials, and this trend is likely to continue given environmental concerns and rising resource prices. The most successful future economies are therefore likely to be those that can create value using fewer expensive inputs, including people. This means materials and labour reduction, alongside efficiencies in transport and distribution, will create a boom in digital, or virtual, products, services and information.

timeline

2011
Apple introduces
iCloud

2016
TripAdvisor more
profitable than Hilton
hotel group

2022
Most valuable company in
the world doesn't actually
make anything

Changing our world Digital information and services obviously still require physical inputs to create and consume them, and are especially reliant on expensive energy, something that people reading e-books or doing Internet searches somehow forget. Nevertheless, with digital products and services, the inputs tend to be smaller and less expensive than with conventional manufacturing and distribution processes. This, in large part, explains the significant difference in financial valuations between old-school industries such as car manufacturing or airlines and new economy industries, for example, social media that are focused on digital ownership and exchange. Farmville, for instance, an application used on Facebook (i.e. a company with no tangible products), has had a valuation of around $5 billion.

> **The change from atoms to bits is irrevocable and unstoppable. Why now? Because the change is also exponential – small differences of yesterday can have suddenly shocking consequences tomorrow.**
>
> **Nicholas Negroponte,**
> **co-founder of MIT Media Lab**

Shift to virtual

'The weightless economy' is a phrase used to describe the fact that much of what's made nowadays doesn't weigh anything – which is much the same as saying that much of the value generated in developed economies comes from information and services, not from manufactured products. So what? The first implication is that location will matter less. Where something is made is largely irrelevant if it's virtual. Second, if a product or service is virtual then the cost of making and distributing many is barely different from making just one. Therefore, it can often make sense to give a product or service away. Third, if we move towards digital products and services, it's easy to personalize them, often to a market of just one.

2026	2028	2029	2039
Photographs no longer owned, but rented	Libraries totally virtual	Google valued at $1.9 trillion	65 per cent of children no longer attend physical schools

Buying and selling nothing

What happens if the economic downturn stops you from buying a $3,000 Gucci bag? Simple. Buy a virtual version of the same bag for $4 instead. Virtual Greats is a US-based company that acts as a broker between brands and celebrities to get their products on sale in virtual worlds such as Gaia or Second Life online – where people spend real money to buy virtual goods, including clothing and virtual land. Profit margins are a healthy 70–90 per cent, largely because the products don't actually exist. Distribution is virtually nil and so too is manufacturing.

Digitalization also means that work itself is changing. Many jobs are no longer tied to a physical location and there's now no reason why you can't live in London and work in New York or share a job with someone many thousands of miles away. Moreover, digitalization means that jobs can be broken down into smaller parts, which people can then bid to work on from across the globe, although this often means that price, alongside quality, is driven down to the point where skills become mere commodities.

One issue to watch seriously is what this all means for intellectual property. As more and more becomes digitalized and virtualized, there is greater opportunity for abuse, although I would expect the area of copyright eventually to catch up with this.

Another example of dematerialization is cloud-computing – rather than physically owning or storing something at a set physical location you can simply pay to gain access to it 'from the air' on any device you like whenever you need it. This might be business information or it could be films, games, photographs and many other items that used to be physically owned and kept by individuals or institutions. Hence, a more general shift away from individual ownership to shared access, which, coincidently, links with a shift from products in general to the more ethereal world of experiences.

The trend even extends to human relationships, which are increasingly facilitated, consummated, mediated and terminated in a virtual rather than a physical manner. For example, voice-based communication (i.e. phone calls to other people), is declining in many countries, while text-based communications are exploding. On one level this is fine. In many cases it's faster, more convenient and cheaper to use text rather than voice. But there's a cost. It is very difficult to convey tone using text, so the opportunity for making mistakes and misunderstanding increases. Hopefully, an increasing use of face-time (via skype or another multidimensional medium) will change this.

> **❝If the books in the cloud are accessed via user interfaces that encourage mashups of fragments that obscure the context and authorship of each fragment, there will be only one book.❞**
>
> **Jaron Lanier, computer scientist and author**

The flip side Of course, where there's a trend there's often a counter trend moving in the opposite direction, so expect to see more interest in the physical in many areas of life. Books, for instance, may become more valued in paper form if the majority of reading is done online or via screens. Similarly, the sending of paper cards or handwritten letters will become important once again if more or less everyone is sending digital greetings and texting condolences. Craft, provenance and history will also matter more if products all start looking and feeling the same. You will, no doubt, be able to buy this book in 'e' or electronic form, but a 'p' version, whose cover and pages wear over time, acquiring an individual physical history, may be more interesting.

Nevertheless, it's likely that developments in screen technology (especially flexible 3D screens, and e-paper), artificial intelligence and what may one day become a more sensory and more immersive Internet mean that, over the longer term, any analogue swings will be all but wiped out by a widespread migration to the virtual realm.

the condensed idea
More virtual goods and services

28 Income polarization

For the top 10 per cent of UK earners, wages increased by roughly 400 per cent between 1978 and 2008. For the bottom 10 per cent the increase was less than 30 per cent. In the USA, income polarization has been more startling. Why is this happening? One reason is globalization. The other is technology.

Could we revert to a feudal society where a tiny slice of the population owns almost everything and lives in isolated and secure splendour, while the vast heaving mass of humanity exists in a constant state of hand-to-mouth uncertainty and desperation? In the UK, a survey found that FTSE 100 CEO pay increased by 32 per cent during 2010. Compare this to the 27 per cent rise low-income earners received in the 30 years from 1978 to 2008, even though overall UK GDP doubled over the same time period. The rewards enjoyed by the top of society are often immensely different than those at the bottom and the danger is that we are creating another 'let them eat cake' society.

The global effect Income polarization, and to some extent stagnating real wages, can be explained by globalization and connective technologies. If you have a skill that's in demand, the market is now global and many of the physical barriers that would have prevented you from competing globally have fallen away. For example, if you're a talented football player living in Latvia you're now free to move elsewhere in Europe – and possibly farther – which 10 per cent of the Latvian population have now done since joining the EU. Furthermore, as a talented sportsperson, your salary is now dictated by global, rather than local, market forces.

timeline

2011	2013	2014	2017
Occupy Wall Street protests about income distribution and fairness	Stagnating incomes in West and North compared to East and South	Hackers target payrolls of investment banks	Muggings in Notting Hill known as 'income tax'

> **The more the division of labour and the application of machinery extend, the more does competition extend among the workers, the more do their wages shrink together.**
>
> **Karl Marx,** sociologist, economist, philosopher and revolutionary

Similarly, if you manufacture a product that people want, you're nowadays less constrained by geographical factors, which can mean bigger financial wins, but the converse is also true. If you have a skill that can be easily outsourced or automated – or you have an outdated skill or no skill at all – you are now more vulnerable.

Taken to the extreme, this situation could eventually mean that self-perpetuating elites are created in certain fields. Entry to such an elite would be almost impossible unless you had the money to afford a certain kind of education (which you wouldn't have unless you were already part of the elite). Perhaps technology will go this way?

Larry Summers, a Harvard economist, says that the economic boom that ended in 2008 was different from previous economic booms in one fundamental way. According to Summers, US employees usually receive around 75 per cent of corporate income, but since 2001 this has fallen to 25 per cent. What this means is a huge disparity between the fortunes of labour and capital over recent years. Corporations have prospered, thanks largely to cost-saving technology and outsourced labour, but prosperity for ordinary households has been an illusion based on cheap borrowing.

Add to this weakened trade unions and declining social mobility and it's possible that many of the features of modern society that people in developed economies have taken for granted for a generation or two may start to go backwards in the future, especially in Western nations where

2022	**2039**	**2080**
Maximum of 100:1 salary ratio widely adopted in Fortune 500 companies	1 billion US dollar millionaires globally	World's first trillionaire

> **The greatest wealth is to live content with little.**
>
> Plato, Ancient Greek philosopher

indebtedness is impacting on the provision of basic public services such as education, health, policing and transport. At the very least, income – and with it opportunity – is likely to polarize, along with the distribution of human dignity and humiliation.

Competing with everyone Stagnating real incomes largely stem from a global power shift and outsourcing from West to East plus the effects of automation. And if you think this is problematic now, just wait a few more years. In the West people are used to the East setting prices for relatively inexpensive consumer goods, but what will it be like if the region sets the global price for labour too? A likely response to all this, especially in the USA and Europe, is economic protectionism. But bucking global trends is unlikely to work over the longer term. One solution would perhaps be to educate people to accept the low-paid jobs that remain locally. A better solution would be to give people better skills, especially in new industries or in industries that do not automate or travel well.

What is the most likely outcome? A dystopian European future might be that excessive environmental regulation, workers rights' and social policies

10,000 to 1

Putting to one side the issue of whether it's ethically right for one person to earn thousands of times more than another, the knowledge that someone is earning a huge sum can cause problems. Unfortunately, it will become increasingly difficult to keep income secret. The Internet and digital data would seem to suggest that keeping everyone else in blissful ignorance of your financial success will become harder and this may trigger not only resentment, but protest and potentially crime. However, the relationship between austerity and inequality and anger and violence is unclear and difficult to separate from other factors. And perhaps it won't matter. If most people have jobs and money to spend they will presumably care less than if they are unemployed or have declining real incomes.

Let them eat cake

A book called *Fault Lines*, by Raghuram Rajan, claims that increased inequality and the response to it, helped to cause the recent economic crisis. In 2007, the richest 1 per cent of American households had 18.3 per cent of income, compared to 18.4 per cent in 1929. Yet from 1952 to 1986, the richest 1 per cent earned less than 10 per cent. Mr Rajan says that technological change increased relative demand for skilled workers, leaving other workers behind. Rather than spend on education and training, governments gave the less skilled workers access to credit. The US government pressured lenders to make loans to poorer people, pushing the share of subprime mortgages from less than 4 per cent in 2000 to 15 per cent just before the crash.

add costs to already globally uncompetitive industries, and taxation will soar to balance the books. A middling scenario might be that workers acknowledge that they will have to work for longer, with poorer job security, just to make ends meet. In both scenarios, social mobility would presumably decrease, while social unrest and anger would rise.

A best-case scenario (for the West) might be that the East finds it harder than expected to reproduce Western-style innovation and entrepreneurship and demographics cause areas of the East to run out of low-cost labour. Labour costs would then rise to similar levels globally, while the West retains an advantage in value-adding industries. In the middle of this muddle one thing does seem clear. Free-market capitalism works only when rewards are shared, at least in proportion to effort.

the condensed idea
The rich will get richer

29 What (& where) is work?

Do you remember work? I'm not insinuating that you don't have a job, but am alluding instead to the idea that linear jobs, easily defined, often available for life and generally conducted from a bricks-and-mortar office or factory, have, in many instances, vanished. In their place we have digital nomads, juggling projects and feverishly scanning data from 'hot desks' in coffee shops.

Jana, previously called Txteagle, is the largest employer in Kenya, founded in 2008 by a computer engineer called Nathan Eagle. It has 10,000 workers in Kenya, but does not pay a penny for office space to house any of them. In fact, the company's founder has never met most of its employees. Txteagle sends small jobs to anyone with access to a mobile phone. The jobs are tiny – little bits of translation, a quick market research survey, or a handful of images to be tagged – each of which pays just a few cents each.

To some extent, Jana is simply a tale of a savvy entrepreneur and the way companies are chopping up big tasks into small bits, aided by technology. But it's also a story about the future of work, especially the way in which independent or freelance workers are taking over from salaried employees. According to the US Government Accountability Office, such jobs – 'contingent workers' in jargon-speak – already make up a third of the US workforce. This trend is starting to make some people rethink what a job actually is or could be in the future. Of course, a job is more than just a series of tasks. Jobs (especially full-time jobs) provide economic stability and identity. So if employers break up each position into a series

timeline

2015	2025	2030
Workers bid online for salaries, with jobs going to lowest bidders	Holographic telepresence widely used in meetings	Part-time work redefined as 1,000- or 2,000-hour jobs rather than 40-hour weeks

of projects or tasks, they run the risk of threatening both. Jobs also provide legal security, healthcare, pensions and other benefits. Or at least they used to.

But beyond considering why people need work it's worth pausing to consider what else will affect the future of work and how the nature of jobs themselves will change. The list of factors impacting on work is a long one, and includes: globalization, automation, digitalization, artificial intelligence, workforce ageing, skilled labour shortages, job mobility, open collaboration, outsourcing, transparency, business ethics, educational practices, regulatory changes, fluid networks, resource shortages, climate change, shifts in organizational structures and the impact of more women in the workforce.

Women at work This last factor is especially significant. A generation or two ago women were largely absent from the workforce in many countries or were restricted to relatively menial jobs. Furthermore, this

> ❛**The best way to appreciate your job is to imagine yourself without one.**❜
>
> **Oscar Wilde, writer and poet**

Dying jobs

- Shorthand secretary
- Switchboard operator
- Receptionist
- Bookbinder
- Printer
- Typist
- Supermarket cashier
- Photo-processor

- Toll-booth operator
- Video store owner
- Call centre operator
- Data-entry clerk
- Record store manager
- Fighter pilot
- Newspaper delivery boy

- Freight-handler
- Butcher
- Baker
- Candlestick maker
- Translator
- Unskilled agricultural worker
- Computer operator
- Lift operator

- Errand boy
- Mail clerk/post boy
- Order clerk
- Train driver
- Bank teller
- Travel agent
- Blacksmith
- Roof thatcher
- Cinema projectionist

2035	2040	2045	2050
Onsite childcare and aged care become commonplace in offices	Organizations start to offer scholarships to children as young as five	Phasing out of formal retirement age for all men and women	Most people work for themselves

> **The underlying source of anguish for many people in work today is an antiquated system of employment and management designed for an industrial age.**
>
> **Richard Donkin,**
> **writer and columnist**

revolution has taken place with relatively little friction. A few nations defy the trend, but skills shortages and ageing populations will almost certainly result in even more women being brought into the workforce in the future.

Why has this happened? One reason is political, but a stronger factor has been the expansion of higher education. What are the implications of more women at work? One consequence could be a slight feminization of organizational structures, leadership styles and even the regulatory environment. Put simply, if more women are in charge of large organizations such as PepsiCo or the International Monetary Fund (IMF), then we might expect more female-friendly policies to come to the fore. This isn't happening everywhere and progress in some areas is painfully slow. Nevertheless, the rise of the service sector over manufacturing could be seen as an example of how female brains are making a mark over male muscle. In the EU, 6 million of the 8 million new jobs that appeared between 2000 and 2009 were filled by women, and in the USA, female-owned businesses employ more workers than the biggest 500 companies put together. Goldman Sachs, the global investment bank, estimates that in Italy and Spain, increasing the number of women in work to a level comparable to men would boost GDP by 21 per cent and 19 per cent respectively.

As a result, expect to see a growth in flexible contracts and conditions and more focus on intuition and empathy. The rising numbers of women in workforces may very well lead to lower pay too: women are often in areas where work is poorly paid and in some instances pay drops to fit the number of women available to do the work.

Closer to home As for the nature of jobs themselves, we will see more part-time and flexible working, more working from home (more working from anywhere at any time, in fact), more job specialization and the rising importance of what some people have termed the right-brain professions. This refers to work that can't be done well by highly intelligent machines or outsourced to highly intelligent people in lower-cost countries: nurses, teachers, architects, writers, poets,

Jobs that don't yet exist

- Sensory Internet engineer
- Virtual currency financial planner
- Personal avatar designer
- Generational conflict counsellor
- Human organ farmer
- Digital information curator

- Hacker relationship manager
- Waste data expert
- Space travel agent
- Personal reputation consultant
- Chief privacy officer
- Vertical farmer

- Climate reversal consultant
- Wealth dispersal consultant
- Third-age travel agent
- Austerity advisor
- Intellectual property developer
- Head of corporate ethics
- Robot relationship counsellor

painters, musicians, philosophers and plumbers along with certain scientists, designers, engineers, lawyers, stress counsellors, masseurs, religious ministers, and a host of policy-makers, strategists, innovators and entrepreneurs.

Of course, all of the above is rather general. In reality, the situation will vary enormously from one country to another, although attracting and assimilating immigrants to offset declining fertility rates and rising wage rates will be an issue for most. Some nations, notably Japan and South Korea, will embrace automation – and especially robotics – to solve this problem, while others may try measures ranging from temporary citizenship to awarding citizenship only if you agree to certain conditions, such as time spent in specific geographical locations, industries, professions or even the armed forces.

the condensed idea
Work will change

30 The pursuit of happiness

Politics and economics have historically been dominated by the idea of income and consumption being linked to happiness, especially in the West. The more an individual earns, the more content and secure he or she is supposed to feel, and the same principle works with countries too. But if more people are working harder and earning more money, why aren't more of us feeling happier as a result?

It wasn't so long ago that individuals were in large part defined by their job, car, home and their various material possessions, with the accumulation of the most consumer goods during our lifetime seen as somehow implying status or success. It was certainly supposed to make us all happy.

How we'll spend money But things are changing. In developing regions, rapidly rising incomes are creating an era of manic materialism, but this will eventually slow down, especially when people see that additional income does not necessarily equate to additional happiness. As individuals get richer, their spending will shift from ostentatious goods to more discrete services. A shift will also occur from spending on goods that are externally directed (cars, clothes and so on) to items that are less visible to the outside world. Initially people will want to show off, but eventually this will wear off.

Add to this the fact that many people will no longer have the promise of a job for life, and perhaps more individuals will feel anxious about expensive

timeline

1972	2004	2010	2012
Term 'Gross National Happiness' coined by the King of Bhutan	Downshifting movement gains momentum	Self-storage industry worth more than Hollywood	The cloud facilitates a move away from physical ownership

long-term financial commitments. As a result, they'll be forced to question what it is that they need and whether they actually have to own or acquire certain items. Money will still feature in the future, but it may not be quite as important as it is now, especially if more of us start to question the fundamentals of ownership.

Technology, for example, is changing how, what and where we consume. If you need a car, you can now have one without actually owning one. Mobile connectivity means that you can find a car, drive it off and pay for it with just a mobile phone. It is time-share brought up-to-date with collaborative, connective technologies. Or how about that job? The job for life might have gone, but technology is starting to break the link between jobs and physical location (see Chapter 29).

> **'We have no more right to consume happiness without producing it than to consume wealth without producing it.'**
>
> **George Bernard Shaw,**
> **playwright and co-founder of the**
> **London School of Economics**

2032 Happiness League Table

1 Denmark	8 = Australia	18 = Unified Korea
2 Finland	8 = Switzerland	20 Republic of Western Australia
3 Norway	12 = Panama	21 Venezuela
4 Sweden	12 = Brazil	22 Unified Ireland
5 Netherlands	14 = United States	23 = Puerto Rico
6 = Costa Rica	14 = South Belgium	23 = Iceland
6 = New Zealand	16 Scottish Republic	25 Welsh Republic
8 = Canada	17 New England	26 Moon Base Alpha
8 = South Sudan	18 = Mexico	

Source: Hallup World Poll 2032

2013	**2023**	**2039**	**2050**
Rising demand for psychological and therapeutic services	Government attempts to measure individual happiness on an annual basis	Happiness industry bigger than self-storage industry and Hollywood combined	Study says search for happiness is making most people miserable

> **❝Our greatest happiness does not depend on the condition of life in which chance has placed us, but is always the result of a good conscience, good health, occupation, and freedom in all just pursuits.❞**
>
> **Thomas Jefferson, diplomat and US President**

In theory this will create greater flexibility, and perhaps more happiness, although in other cases the exact reverse is more likely, with people becoming anxious due to a lack of certainty.

A question of value Mix this all up and in the future I suspect that more people will question the very idea and value of 'things'. For instance, why is GDP measured purely in terms of economic output regardless of the damage the output might be doing to individuals, the environment or society as a whole? Shouldn't general happiness be factored in and why should societies allow individuals to do or acquire certain things if there is a substantial negative cost to the rest of society? Happiness has always been difficult to measure, but there is plenty of evidence to show that once discomfort has been banished, additional income does not make people any happier.

Part of the problem is that business has taken over most aspects of life. There are fewer boundaries between home and work. As a result, we work longer and harder and our relationships are pushed to the margin. Communities suffer too when business and profit come to the fore, as public services are closed down because they are 'uneconomic'.

Perhaps one of the unforeseen consequences of an individualistic society is that people eventually become less happy, because they are individually responsible for their own success or failure, and while few of us won't admit it, we do ultimately fail at what we do far more than we succeed. In past times, we had family, community, religion (see Chapter 49) and even class to shield us from this truth.

What else, apart from happiness, will people want in the future? My answer would be that people will want their existence to be recognized.

Is everyone happy?

A social psychologist at the University of Leicester in the UK has created a 'World Map of Happiness' using statistical data plus responses from 80,000 people across the world. Top of the happiness list of 178 countries is Denmark followed by Switzerland, Austria and Iceland. Britain ranks 41st and the USA came in at 23 based on various indicators including health, poverty levels and access to education. Bottom of the list was Zimbabwe. There were a few surprises too. Capitalist countries came out relatively well, while countries that are supposed to have a powerful sense of collective identity scored less well. For example, China ranked 82, Japan 90 and India 125.

They will want someone, somewhere, to respect them and tell that they've achieved something worthwhile. They will want job security and protection for when things go wrong, meaningful work, enough money, freedom from violence and abuse and a community that cares for everyone. Importantly, once basic needs have been met, there will also be an increasing desire for more psychological or philosophical engagement or fulfilment. We will seek control, simplicity and above all meaningful relationships with other human beings, especially when much of what is around us becomes artificial, virtual, digital and machine-based.

Ultimately the challenge for society is to figure out how to deliver all this. One solution is for us to become less self-absorbed and individualistic and more community-orientated. Add to this a shared vision of where we're all heading, and one by-product of our restless quest might eventually be happiness.

the condensed idea
Measuring what
really matters

31 Human beings version 2.0

'Steve Austin. A man barely alive. Gentlemen, we can rebuild him. We have the technology.' That was back in 1974 and the *The Six Million Dollar Man* was science fiction. But wait. It's the 21st century and we do now have the technology. We have bionic ears, artificial limbs, IVF, pacemakers and full-face transplants, and in the future we'll start to merge with our machines.

We already rebuild and adapt our bodies. We even attempt, usually in a rather clumsy way, to fix or improve our minds. So at what point do we cease to be human and become something else? Shane Warne playing cricket with glasses or contact lenses and a new hairstyle would be considered, by most people, to be fairly normal. But what happens if he replaces a perfectly good arm with a prosthetic arm to improve the speed of his bowling? Is that serious cheating or just practical self-improvement? Or should a double amputee with prosthetic limbs be allowed to compete in the able-bodied 100m final and, if so, could he be said to suffer from an advantage or a disadvantage?

Real or not? Humans have been adapting themselves to different environments and conditions since the dawn of existence. We have also been attempting to improve our health, speed, strength and mental abilities for almost as long. But what started with clothes, shoes, a haircut and a set of glasses has rapidly progressed to the point where it's becoming difficult to tell who's real and who's not. Are a fake tan, dyed hair, breast enlargement and teeth whitening just someone competing for a mate or someone who is somehow cheating?

timeline   Ma = million years ago

15 Ma	3–4 Ma	1.3–1.8 Ma
Great apes	First fully bipedal ape	*Homo erectus*

A whole new arm

Dr Rudy Wells: 'I want to show you something, Steve. This is your arm.'

Steve Austin: 'That's it, huh?'

Dr Rudy Wells: 'We're rather proud of it. There's a manual that goes with it that has eight hundred and forty pages. I'll give you a copy.'

From *The Six Million Dollar Man*

And, as usual, you haven't seen anything yet. How about totally artificial hearts, livers, kidneys, or blood, plastic bones, human body parts grown in laboratories, contact lenses featuring data displays and augmented reality, artificial skin that can be synchronized with touch screens to transmit data or be used to display data on itself, direct brain-to-machine interfaces (i.e. thought control), orgasm chips and exoskeletons (skeletons you wear on the outside of your body to increase strength or to prolong mobility in older age). Most of these ideas already exist in research and development laboratories, or soon will, thanks to developments in medicine, engineering, computing, nanotechnology and materials science among other fields.

The challenge is not in building these bits, but whether or not all the bits can be added together. Could we, for example, buy a whole new body if our current one is worn out and just stick our head on top? Or what about a whole new brain? The term 'cosmetic neurology' – essentially plastic surgery for the brain, so could we pick

> **Keep in mind that non-biological intelligence is doubling each year, whereas our biological intelligence is essentially fixed.**
>
> Ray Kurzweil,
> author, inventor and futurist

> # 6 Technology ... the knack of so arranging the world that we don't have to experience it. 9
>
> **Max Frisch,** playwright and author

a new brain or, more likely, various plug-ins to create or enhance specific brain functions – has already been coined. Nuts, I know, but someone would have said that about full-face transplants 50 years ago.

The revolutionary idea is not so much tinkering with the brain, but moving it somewhere else entirely. What if, for example, our understanding of the human brain and human consciousness progresses to such a level that we are able to effectively download our brains into machines? Add some sophisticated robotics for those of us who fancy a bit of walking about, and what you've got, more or less, is immortality. Or perhaps it's *The Matrix*?

I, Machine It is sometimes assumed that human beings are the peak of the evolutionary tree. That evolution has essentially ended with the human species and that people are relatively fixed with regard to physical form – give or take the odd spray tan and some new glasses. But why would that be so? Why would evolution stop now? We are smart, very smart. That's why we're still here. So why wouldn't we merge with our machines and go forth to explore new galaxies? And what exactly does it mean to look or be human anyway?

I think it's ultimately inevitable that we will merge with our technology. This won't happen overnight. It's unlikely to happen in our lifetimes. But, eventually, 100 or 200 years hence, developments in genetics, robotics, the Internet, nanotechnology and artificial intelligence, together with fields and sciences we haven't even named or invented yet, will come together to create a new hybrid species. As the author, inventor and futurist Ray Kurzweil points out, this will most probably begin with tiny nanobots in our bodies and inside our brains. 'The nanobots will keep us healthy, provide full-immersion virtual reality from within the nervous system, provide direct brain-to-brain communication over the Internet and greatly expand human intelligence.'

In what do we trust?

Is a human or a machine best suited to a three-year space voyage? In theory, a machine would seem more psychologically suited, but what if mankind wanted to go to Mars and back rather than see a machine do it? Moreover, are there some things that we would want to prevent machine-modified men and women from doing? Would you trust a modified human being (one of the early human-robot hybrids) with a small child? How about modified politicians? Would you be more trusting of a biological human Prime Minister at Number 10 Downing Street? Or would you be perfectly happy with one who had spent considerable sums of money on sophisticated brain augmentation?

We may, ultimately, become creatures of pure consciousness, able to move at will between physical bodies and machines. Or perhaps we'll be confined to certain forms dependent upon our intelligence, behaviour or an ability to pay. Would this be something that people would want? Would it be progress? The answer to the first question is that some of us probably would. As for progress, this word is meaningless in the absence of an objective or goal. What exactly would we be progressing towards, and would such developments be a movement in the right direction? Perhaps such developments will create a new Age of Enlightenment. Maybe we'll be enslaved by our own creations, or possibly we'll find out that the future doesn't need us at all.

the condensed idea
Merger of man and machine

32 Brain–machine interfaces

Forget keyboards, computer mice, gesture-based computing or synthesized speech – we will soon have brain-to-machine interfaces that link the human brain directly to various external devices. So, in the future, we'll still ask computer technicians for an upgrade, but it will be for us, not our computers.

Brain–machine interfaces – or brain–computer interfaces – have existed in research laboratories for a while, especially in labs working to create computer interfaces for people unable to use their hands or other parts of their bodies. In 1995 direct brain-to-machine control surfaced in, of all places, toy shops, with toys such as the Star Wars Force Trainer and Mindflex. So how much longer are you going to have to wait until the problem of finding the lost TV remote is solved by direct brain-to-television channel-changing headgear? The answer is possibly not very long. Apple is already rumoured to be working on a smart TV that doesn't need a remote because you just talk to the television when you need it to do something.

Assistive technologies have been around for a long time. Wheelchairs are an early example, but in the future they will probably be controlled by thought as well as via joysticks. Or what if people with disabilities could have electrodes implanted or wear a skullcap that connected their brain directly to an artificial limb? Both more or less exist already, as do various brain–machine interfaces to treat memory disorders of ageing, especially serious diseases such as Alzheimer's and Parkinson's. Sometimes this technology uses

timeline

2000	2001	2006	2008
Electrode arrays implanted into owl monkeys	Technology allows a monkey to operate a robotic arm via thought control	Teenager plays Space Invaders using brain signals	Scientists manage to extract images from a person's mind

non-invasive electrodes placed on the scalp of a patient; in other instances electrodes are implanted directly inside the patient's brain. The advantage of implants is accuracy of commands.

So what's next? First up are many more medical applications, especially for people suffering from verbal communication problems or movement disorders. Severely disabled individuals or those suffering from 'locked in syndrome' would be prime candidates for such neural interfaces.

Then we may see the human brain being linked to various appliances and consumer devices ranging from cars and refrigerators to household lighting. Wouldn't it be great, for instance, if you could just think 'lights on' and your lights switched themselves on, or 'oven on' and on it goes? Or maybe not. After all, our bodies need some physically activity to prevent them wasting away. But perhaps even this problem can be solved using implants that stimulate our muscles.

> **We don't know what the limits are yet.**
>
> **Melody Moore Jackson,**
> **Georgia Tech University's**
> **BrainLab**

All done for you

It's 7 a.m. There is sun poking through the curtains in your bedroom, so you think about opening them along with a small window to let in some fresh air. Both the curtains and the window immediately oblige. You then get out of bed and walk into the bathroom and the shower starts running the moment you think about it. It looks a little hot so you think about adding some cold water and the steam starts to disappear. Downstairs you pass the coffee machine, which has already dispensed some coffee because it's synchronized to turn itself on once the curtains are opened. At this point your fridge reminds you that you should do five minutes' exercise to offset the lack of physical tasks already encountered at the start of your day. Is this your idea of heaven or hell?

2009	2017	2026
Brain–Twitter interface	Voice control replaces 70 per cent of keyboards	Google patents neural interface

❛We're moving ahead so rapidly, it's not going to be that long before we will be able to tell whether someone's making up a story, or whether someone intended to do a crime with a certain degree of certainty.❜

Barbara Sahakian, **Professor of Neuropsychology, Cambridge University**

Data download The dream, to some extent, is to allow people to download data directly into their brains. This could be useful from an educational point of view, enabling students to implant thoughts directly into their heads, or perhaps it might one day allow people to download or share their own dreams. It would certainly take computer gaming to a new level, and introduces some intriguing philosophical questions concerning reality.

It also raises the question of whether we'll one day be able to read other peoples' brains remotely to find out what they're thinking or what they're planning to do in the future, which takes us directly to that classic sci-fi movie *Minority Report* and the Department of Future Crime. Again, it sounds somewhat fanciful, but I can almost guarantee that one day society will be having debates about ethical issues surrounding electronic eavesdropping on our innermost thoughts or on the probing of future intentions.

And what of animals? This is most definitely fringe thinking, but it's possible that consciousness exists as a continuum, with animals and even plants having varying degrees of consciousness. If this were to be true, and we could find a way of tapping into this and communicating with them, it would literally be mind-blowing, not least because a major justification for killing animals ethically is the fact that they are not self-aware, or do not have knowledge of their own existence, in quite the same fundamental way that we human beings do. Can you imagine, for example, if we suddenly found a way to communicate with dolphins and they told us what they thought of us?

Force-powered telekinesis

A few years ago I bought a Star Wars Force Trainer toy in Sydney, Australia, for about AUD$150. It was for me. I wanted to see whether it was really possible to use a brain–machine interface (headset) to send brain waves to the toy, which would then start up a motorized fan that would send a small ping-pong ball up a tube. Did it work? Up to a point, although I get more use from my ballpoint pen that translates handwritten text into digital files and can make audio and video recordings of important meetings.

What do we really know? On another level, future possibilities include living in a world where almost any manmade device *can* be accessed, questioned or controlled by thought alone and where communication between individuals, even those geographically distant, is facilitated by a form of mental telepresence or psychic sixth-sense technology.

Once again, this probably sounds fanciful. But it's not impossible. Furthermore, if and when we do enter this realm, a number of questions emerge. The first is how will we know that we really exist in the way that we think we do? Perhaps we've always been living inside a computer simulation? If the simulation was sophisticated enough and determined the exact inputs fed to our brains, how could we tell the difference? This would be unpleasant if we couldn't control it, but imagine the possibilities if we could. It's not time travel or teleportation, but it's getting very close.

the condensed idea
Thought control

33 Avatar assistants

Computer-based avatars are virtual recreations of real or fictional characters used in forms of computer gaming and in virtual online communities. In the near future they will become common as intelligent digital assistants or personal agents, controlled by forms of artificial intelligence such as natural language processing and accessed via mobile or fixed devices.

Apple's iPhone 4S offers a tantalizing glimpse of the future in the form of Siri, an application that allows users to employ normal language to send messages or ask questions. But this is a very basic technology compared with what's to come.

> **Everything is backwards now, like out there is the true world, and in here is the dream.**
>
> **Jake Sully** in the movie *Avatar*

In a decade, probably less, we will have available personal digital or avatar-based assistants in a variety of forms (human beings, aliens, animals, fantasy characters, celebrities), which are animated and have personalities. We will use them as secretaries, assistants, playthings and occasionally partners to help us navigate the Web, understand the world and get things done. Basic versions of what might also be called synthetic personalities, digital humans or digital 'bots' already exist in customer services roles on websites, usually to save money or to deal with frequently asked questions.

In the future, avatar assistants will replace NHS Direct. It will be them you contact when you have a question about an injury or medical

timeline

1974	1979	1987	1993	1999	2000
Maze War	MUD	Max Headroom	Doom	Everquest	Ananova

condition and they will talk to you, explain what's possibly wrong and fix an appointment with a real nurse or doctor (or perhaps a robotic surgeon or a medical diagnosis algorithm). They will be used as assistants in education, especially younger-years schooling, where they will teach repetitive, rules-based tasks such as language or mathematics. They will also appear in aged care, reminding elderly people to take their medicine or simply acting as digital companions. It's also likely that they will form the interface – or just the face – between people and robots or other machines in the future.

What makes an avatar? The basic technology behind avatars is artificial intelligence, especially natural voice processing, but this will evolve, like most things, as will technologies such as individual face and

Man v machine

Is there anything about the interaction between one human being and another that cannot be replicated by a machine? More specifically, would it be possible to form a strong emotional bond with an intelligent avatar assistant and could this relationship replace, or even surpass, a physical relationship with another person? For such a relationship, several things would need to happen. First, technology will need to advance to a stage where someone can have a truly meaningful conversation with a machine. Second, societal values will need to shift so that it's seen as acceptable to withdraw from other people. Third, there will need to be a way of generating physical sensations – either by avatars taking on some kind of physical form, by allowing people to touch objects in virtual worlds via haptic technology or through a form of full sensory immersion achieved via brain implants or pharmaceuticals.

2002	2003	2004	2011	2012	2032
The Sims Online	Second Life	World of Warcraft	Apple Siri	Evi iPhone and Android app available as a 69p download	70 per cent of adults use intelligent avatar personal assistants

voice recognition. Avatars will be able to identify specific individuals and personalize their reactions as a result. They will also be connected to the Internet (and therefore to other avatars and, indeed, to more or less everything else in both physical and digital domains), so their knowledge will be fairly impressive. They could even be programmed to have a sense of humour and to display various humanoid features such as body language and emotion.

Avatar assistants will also be highly personalizable in the sense that regional accents could be chosen or human personality flaws and moods added. There may even be the option to make the personality of an avatar assistant mirror that of its 'owner', or perhaps an owner might start to adapt their own personality to their avatar – something referred to as the Proteus Effect.

What exactly will people do with their avatars? Nobody really knows, because the basic versions that do already exist are rather limited in terms of their abilities and because we haven't really got used to using them yet. As for the more sophisticated versions, they are still in their infancy in research laboratories. A good guess: most of the things that we currently ask human assistants, friends, family and even lovers to do. We will ask them where to find things, and we will go to them for advice, reassurance and companionship. We will ask them how things work, why things are they way that they are, or whether what we're doing is really worthwhile.

> **'Electric communication will never be a substitute for the face of someone who with their soul encourages another person to be brave and true.'**
> **Charles Dickens, author**

Is love on the cards? As to whether someone could ever form a strong emotional bond, or even fall in love, with an avatar, why not? In theory, it would be no different from maintaining a long-distance relationship over the telephone or online, or having an infatuation with a celebrity on television. And, once again, don't forget that they will be connected to the Internet, which will itself be connected to virtually everything else. Therefore you will be able to ask your avatar assistant to run you a bath or play computer games with you. You could ask them to remind you where you bought your shoes and how much you paid for them, as well as how far you'd walked in them, when they'll need to be repaired and who is the nearest person – or machine

eLoves me

According to a Pew Internet study, 26 per cent of Americans know someone who has dated someone they met online. A further 31 per cent also know someone who has looked for love online. Academic researchers are developing special algorithms, sophisticated questionnaires and data-mining techniques to predict romantic compatibility for matchmaking websites. This works, in part, because of scale. If you have enough people visiting a site – and you have the right data-mining techniques – you can build predictive models that deconstruct love to a simple formula. But why limit this to human beings? If you can predict what people are looking for, why not build avatars that can emotionally bond with people?

– to do this. You could even ask your avatar to be 'you' in distant meetings, possibly representing you as a hologram (they would, of course, be able to record any meetings as audio or video files, then play them back to you later).

Impossible? Certainty not. Recording conference calls and virtual meetings is already a practical proposition. And consider this: in 2012 a hologram allowed the dead rapper Tupac Shakur to perform 'live' in front of fans with another musician. So using holographic telepresence to be somewhere else, or be in more than one place at once, is a real possibility.

Quite where all this will leave human relationships is anyone's guess. Perhaps we'll become incapable of directly relating to other human beings unless the relationship is mediated via an avatar or electronic device. Some might say this is happening already.

the condensed idea
Imaginary friends

34 Uncanny Valley

'Uncanny resemblance' is a term often used to describe something or, more usually, someone, who looks strangely or spookily familiar. In robotics the term 'Uncanny Valley' is used to describe how people instinctively reject robots that look too much like human beings, the valley in question being a trough in a graph showing robot rejection and acceptance.

The word 'robot' comes from the Czech word, meaning 'servitude', although some translations use the terms 'obligatory work', 'forced labour' or 'drudgery'. Most popular visions of the future include robots, often with human-like forms, and with other features mimicking human height, eyes, limbs, movement and even human conversation. But this is precisely where the trouble starts.

We have become accustomed to the idea of robots making other machines, cars, for example, and we are now getting used to robots in the form of cuddly toys, lawnmowers, vacuum cleaners and bomb-disposal machines. The Japanese are apparently even getting used to R2-D2-like nursery assistants and aged care robots. But what happens when someone builds a humanoid-like bot that looks and acts like, well, one of us? To some extent we already know.

What do we fear? In Japan, for example, Dr Hiroshi Ishiguro has created a robot that looks like ... Dr Ishiguro. The resemblance is uncanny, prompting an uncomfortable reaction from observers, especially as 'he' is sporting the same glasses and wears the same clothes. From a distance

timeline

1950	1999	2000	2004
I, Robot short stories by Isaac Asimov	Sony's Aibo dog	Hasbro's FurReal robotic pets	WowWee's Robosapien

you can hardly tell the difference. Interestingly, the idea of such robots tends to be rejected by adults, but is often accepted by young children. Not all young children, though. Before he made a robotic copy of himself, Dr Ishiguro made a lifelike copy of his four-year-old daughter. She was so upset after seeing it that she refused point blank to enter her father's laboratory in case she encountered it again. As to what will happen if robots become so life-like in appearance and mannerisms that you really cannot tell the difference, that's anyone's guess.

Psychologically speaking, we recognize certain types of robot as lifelike – meaning human lifelike – and then we suddenly notice various non-human features or characteristics, which leads to feelings of unease, alienation and even disgust. Perhaps the same could be said of our reactions to dead bodies. Cartoon characters, cartoon-like avatars and cuddly toys, in contrast, do not present the same level of threat because they are not trying to trick us into believing they're human. Perhaps this is linked to some kind of ancient species preservation or protection instinct. Or maybe we've all just been watching too much tech-noir science fiction?

Some people totally reject the whole hypothesis, arguing that it's ridiculous to reduce human

Furry robots

A few years ago Sony announced that it was ending production of its plastic and metal robotic Aibo dog, while toymaker Hasbro has announced that it's expanding its range of 'FurReal' robotic animals. In other words, robotics as robots aren't selling whereas robotically enhanced toys (especially furry ones) are. The Hasbo line-up includes a baby chimpanzee and a miniature pony that's afraid of the dark. Even some of the more 'traditional' robotic toys such as Robosapien conceal their robotic origins. The lesson here is that, apart from a few gadget freaks, most people want robots to do something useful for them such as clean the floor (e.g. the Roomba) or provide an interactive experience that's cuddly rather than menacing or mechanical.

> **The technology is simply an excuse to tell a story about how we should be afraid of the worst parts of ourselves.**
>
> **Mike Jones,**
> **Sydney Powerhouse Museum**

2005	2006	2016	2030
Cornell's first self-replicating robot	Amazing Allysen interactive doll	Widespread use of agricultural robots	98 per cent of Korean homes contain a robot

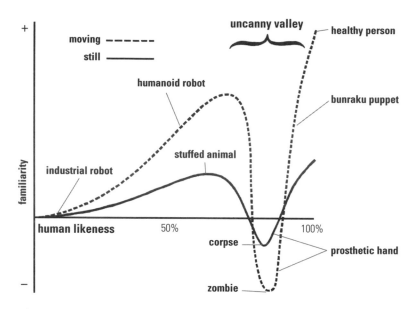

The response of humans to various objects plotted against their human-like characteristics.

authenticity to a single measurement on a graph, but as robotics, virtual reality, artificial intelligence, computer animation and synthetic biology all converge, this debate will get quite complex. This fact has not escaped the attention of artists, such as Patricia Piccinini, who has created human-hybrid sculptures and other controversial artworks. And if you think Patricia's work is a little disturbing, have a look at the reborn 'dolls' created by the photographer Rebecca Martinez for a project called 'pretenders' or the 'lifelike' artworks of Ron Mueck.

> **❝I worry that if kids grow up being taught by robots and viewing technology as the instructor they will see it as the master.❞**
>
> **Mitchel Resnick, Massachusetts Institute of Technology**

Emerging robots But apart from these controversies, what else can we expect from robots in the near future? At the moment the robotics industry is fragmented, with a plethora of standards and platforms, much like the computer industry was in the 1970s. Currently, most robots are also low-volume niche products, ranging from bomb-disposal and surveillance robots used by the military to domestic robots that cut the lawn or sweep the floor. But this will change due to the convergence of a handful of trends. First, the cost of computing power (processing and storage) is dropping fast. Second, distributed computing, voice and visual recognition technologies and wireless broadband connectivity are similarly dropping in price and increasing in availability.

Personal robots could soon be dispensing medicine, folding laundry, teaching kids and keeping an eye open for intruders. There could also be some less obvious uses for robots, especially in customer service roles. For instance, robots could carry your shopping bags in a supermarket or your suitcases in a hotel. They could replace guide dogs for visually impaired people or take over from care workers in nursing homes. Whether a machine will ever fully replace human or animal contact is a big question and will in large part depend on what these robots look like.

Dr Spook

C-3PO from *Star Wars* was cute. Some of the robots coming out of Japan are not. Why the difference? One explanation is evolutionary. At a deep level we may have been programmed to avoid corpses because they're linked to death and disease. And things that are clearly not human, but behave in a human-like manner, are creepy (such as Chucky the doll in the movie *Child's Play*). So too are things that look almost human, but don't act as we expect them to (e.g. the Japanese nurse robot called Actroid-F). The most eerie aspect of these is usually the eyes, when they're combined with unconvincing humanoid movement. Why is that? Possibly because the eyes play a large part in conveying emotion or in some way showing that something is alive.

However, attitudes may shift, especially if humanoid robots start to display synchronous behaviour (e.g. they mimic human gestures) and can learn to be emotional. As for whether people could form strong relationships with robots, that's an open question, although our experience with animals might suggest that we will.

There is little evidence of any inner consciousness in domesticated animals, but we often treat them almost like human companions. Perhaps, by 2050, we will regularly have relationships with robots and even end up, in some cases, marrying them

the condensed idea
We prefer our robots cuddly

35 Transhumanism

Could emerging technologies enable individuals to radically extend life spans or even transcend the very idea of ageing itself? As you might expect, transhumanism has annexed various philosophical ideas, especially in California, to become a kind of quasi-religion or a quest for immortality.

At one level transhumanism intersects with some fairly practical theories regarding life extension. For example, the adoption of a very low-calorie diet has been shown in some studies to significantly extend the life of mice and some say that the idea can be applied to people too. Developments in regenerative medicine (see Chapter 22) tap into some of these urges and impulses too, although beyond this, things can get a little weird.

Some people, for example, believe that it's possible to use cryonics (i.e. low-temperature preservation techniques) to keep dead people in a state of suspended animation until future medical technologies allow them to be brought back to life – although it's much more likely that they'll just be defrosted into a kind of slush. Is this happening already? Yes, in California primarily. Why are people doing this? A quest for immortality or a second chance most probably. Having said this, some scientists argue that the idea is not quite as cranky as it sounds, and point to insects such as the arctic moth, which pauses its growth each winter until its seven-year development has finished.

What's in it for us? More standard versions of transhumism have attracted some serious thinkers over the years, including, most notably, the futurist and inventor Ray Kurzweil and the nanotechnology pioneer

timeline

2100	2150	2200
Human beings start migration to far-flung galaxies	Typical humanoid life span is 584	Children heavily taxed to reduce overcrowding on planet XB-1987

Eric Drexler. Drexler, for example, has speculated about the potential of using nanotechnology to repair worn-out or broken body parts to radically change what it means to be human and potentially extend human life indefinitely. This obviously links with branches of artificial intelligence and robotics thinking, all of which in some way challenge what it means to be human or, in the case of transhumanism, argue that human beings will at some point extend beyond biological constraints to become post-human.

> **Death gives meaning to our lives. It gives importance and value to time. Time would become meaningless if there were too much of it.**
>
> **Ray Kurzweil, author, inventor and futurist**

Some people find transhumanism a somewhat abhorrent idea precisely because it extends the capabilities and especially the longevity of the individual. It seems somewhat selfish and narcissistic, they say, given many of the problems the human race as a whole already faces or will face in the future. However, it may be where extreme forms of individualism eventually take us.

The death of death?

'Death is a very dull, dreary affair, and my advice to you is to have nothing whatever to do with it,' said W. Somerset Maugham. One suspects that whether or not the transhumanists succeed in defeating death will have more to do with economics than technology. If wealth is widespread it's likely that a great number of people will spend their surplus savings on saving themselves. If society is wealthy too it will probably wish them the best of luck. But if the economic environment is harsher, it's unlikely that people will spend what little money they have left launching an offensive against death and it's unlikely that society will support large-scale research into the area either.

2250	2255	2275	2300
Having children is made illegal on Earth	Children kept illegally	Average life span now over 800	Transhumanism declared a giant mistake

> **❛Many would apparently rather bumble around with their eyes closed, trusting in tradition, than look around to see what's about to happen. Yes, it is unnerving, yes, it can be scary. After all, there are entirely new mistakes we are now empowered to make for the first time.❜**
>
> Daniel C. Dennett, cognitive scientist, writer and philosopher

As to the religious linkages, it seems that many supporters of transhumanism are agnostic or atheist. This makes logical sense, because these people are challenging the view that life is god-given and that pure biological (i.e. natural or unenhanced) life is sacred. On the other hand, transhumanist views could link more strongly with some Eastern religions, or perhaps forms of spiritualism, because they seem to be suggesting that our biological, bipedal form is merely a staging post, or a stepping stone, to a more enlightened or fulfilling end state.

The ethics of immortality So, is transhumanism an achievable and thoroughly reasonable long-term goal, the world's most dangerous idea or just utter scientific nonsense? In the next 50 years, I am inclined to think the latter, although taking a much longer-term viewpoint it does at least seem achievable.

But just because technology allows us to do something doesn't mean we always should. Unless basic issues relating to resource and even landmass availability can be solved, there is a fairly convincing argument, currently at least, which says that a world full of people who never die is a very bad idea. Dying, after all, has its uses, especially in terms of the regeneration of ideas. This is a point picked up by Steve Jobs in his Stanford University commencement address:

> 'No one wants to die. Even people who want to go to heaven don't want to die to get there. And yet Death is the destination we all share. No one has ever escaped it. And that is as it should be, because Death is very likely the single best invention of Life. It is Life's change agent. It clears out the old to make way for the new. Right now the new is you, but someday not too long from now, you will gradually become the old and be cleared away.'

Can you predict your own death?

Scientists from Boston University in the USA say they have developed a formula to ascertain whether someone will live to see their 100th birthday. The test, which its developers say is 85 per cent accurate, is based on a scan of the genes of 801 centenarians, who were then compared with 914 other people. Clearly environmental factors play a significant role, but the scientists believe genetic variance plays a vital role too. Alternatively, if you'd like a faster opinion on likely funeral dates just visit deathclock.com

Stirring stuff. But what if Steve was wrong? What if it's only a matter of time before our time on Earth – or elsewhere – is effectively infinite? It cannot be beyond the bounds of human ingenuity to solve or, at the very least, to slow down what has historically been considered to be a natural ageing process. Just think what we could achieve if instead of 80 years we all had 180 years.

Personally, I'm with Steve (and Shakespeare: 'Thou know'st 'tis common; all that lives must die.'). Our time is short and it's this very fact that makes life so precious. If life, or anything else for that matter, were to become infinite, it would then be meaningless and trivial. It's precisely life's rarity, its limited nature, that makes it so priceless, and we should fight to the death to stop immortality from becoming a reality.

the condensed idea
Living forever

36 Alt.Space & space tourism

'Alt.Space' is a term that hasn't quite taken off yet. It's a phrase that is just starting to emerge, used to describe private spaceflight, especially that provided by a new breed of companies intent on offering low-cost access to space through the creation of novel technologies or business models. As such, Alt.Space companies are competing directly with NASA and other national or international government space organizations.

Who, just a few decades ago, would have thought that billionaires would one day be in a race to invade space? The first private passenger on board a rocket (a space tourist) was Dennis Tito, who paid around $10–20 million for a return ticket to the International Space Station via the Russian Space Agency. Others who've taken the trip on a Russian Soyuz rocket include Mark Shuttleworth, Anousheh Ansari, Charles Simonyi and Guy Laliberté. As you can see, space tourism is a bit of a man thing, but this may change.

The Russian Space Agency is no longer allowing paying passengers, but billionaire Richard Branson's Virgin Galactic is currently offering a similar experience, albeit suborbital, for a much more down-to-earth price of $200,000. Other entrepreneurial companies active in this field include Space Adventures and Elon Musk's SpaceX (Elon Musk is the forty-year-old entrepreneur behind PayPal and Tesla Motors).

timeline

1969	2013	2018	2035
First human beings land on the Moon	Space tourist flights delayed by solar flares	Air China offers space flights	Agreement to build first Moon hotel

Rocket man

Space is the next frontier for entrepreneurs, especially high-tech billionaires. Paul Allen, co-founder of Microsoft, has announced a plan to build a commercial spaceship that could be spacebound before 2020. The craft is powered by six jumbo-jet engines and has a wingspan of 115m (380ft), the largest ever for a plane. The idea is to jet up to 9,100m (30,000ft), then use boosters to go into orbit, either to dispatch commercial cargo or to give thrill-seekers a ride they'd never forget.

Space travel for all? So will a 'build it and they will come' school of space tourism work? One suspects not, unless the price drops dramatically so that mere mortals rather than the mega-rich can afford it. But then, the price of technology does tend to reduce significantly over time, so perhaps this idea is not quite so out of this world after all. If affordable space access ever does become available, it would almost certainly be revolutionary.

Virgin Galactic, for example, is leading the way towards a new era of space travel – significantly, by combining carrier aircraft and spaceship. The carrier aircraft (with a wingspan equivalent to that of a Boeing 757) carries the spaceship to an altitude of 15km (9 miles) where it is released.

> **❛It won't be too long before bright young men and women set their eyes on careers in Earth orbit and say: "I want to work 200 kilometres from home – straight up!"❜**
>
> **Arthur C. Clarke,** sci-fi author, inventor and futurist

2039	**2044**	**2061**	**2070**
FedEx starts mail deliveries to the Moon	First Moon tourism	Return of Halley's Comet boosts space-tourism industry	McDonald's opens 'fly-thru' in space

Why space?

Why do so many past visions of the future feature space rockets, moon bases, silver space suits, ray guns and aliens? Shortly after the Great Depression and the end of World War Two, the combination of so much optimism mixed with many of the recently developed technologies, especially rocketry, meant that the only place to go was up, if only to find a new set of bad guys to fight. The interest in space accelerated throughout the late 1950s and hit its peak when President John F. Kennedy announced in 1961 that America would put a man on the surface on the moon by the end of the decade. As JFK said: 'We choose to go to the moon in this decade and do other things, not because they are easy, but because they are hard, because that goal will serve to organize and measure the best of our energies and skills.'

This two-craft system is more economical than using throwaway rockets, and also means the spaceship doesn't need to wait for a suitable window in which to launch. These craft could possibly be used to carry other payloads too. Virgin Galactic has hinted that its craft could be used to launch small satellites, which, if the price was low enough, could be used by all kinds of organizations. This would help to bring the cost down for thrill-seeking passengers who've grown tired of two weeks on a beach in Florida.

Reaching for the skies Consider that the US Federal Aviation Authority (FAA) has already published a set of proposed regulations for space tourism operators. Regulations include everything from flight-crew qualifications to medical requirements and permits. Of course, some passengers might want to stay in space a little longer. In fact, some, such as Daniel H. Wilson, author of *Where's My Jetpack?*, are predicting Moon colonies within a decade or so.

After that we could perhaps expect small hotels with wonderful views back to planet Earth, space theme parks with zero-g gyms and possibly permanent settlements full of shy and retiring billionaires or eco-activists keen to stop the destruction of another landscape. And then, presumably,

> ❝The ultimate objective is to make humanity a multiplanet species. Thirty years from now, there'll be a base on the Moon and on Mars, and people will be going back and forth on SpaceX rockets.❞
>
> **Elon Musk,** engineer and entrepreneur

onwards to other galaxies? Probably not in our lifetimes in any meaningful sense, so in the meantime we'll have to console ourselves with good old-fashioned staycations, eco-tourism, glamping, climate change travel, virtual vacations, spa and sleep holidays, dark tourism, voluntourism, medical tourism and floating hotels. Unless, of course, we can invent low-cost warp drive or teleportation.

Of course, there is another possibility. A good trick in terms of looking towards the far future is to start off by looking at the distant past. Why? Because it's essential to separate cycles and fashion from what's genuinely new and important, and because what appears to be new, or revolutionary, often turns out to be nothing of the sort – and time and money can easily be wasted. Using the past to speculate about the future, we might observe that groups which suffered from religious persecution were among the first to colonize the 'New World', so perhaps similarly persecuted peoples could be among the first pioneers of deep space travel. At the moment, this could be any number of religious groups, although that's probably just another case of projecting our current concerns forward in a linear fashion. Maybe, one day, we'll speak of an astronaut called Christopher in another spaceship called *Columbus*.

the condensed idea
The privatization of space

37 Solar energy from space

How's this for an 'out there' idea? In space there's a lot of sun but no clouds. So why not collect solar energy using giant mirrors and beam energy back to Earth using orbiting lasers or microwave beams. Fringe thinking? At the moment yes, but one day it may become mainstream.

It's highly likely that we'll all be worshipping the Sun in the not-too-distant future. All we'll need to do is capture 1 part in 10,000 of the sunlight that reaches our planet to meet 100 per cent of our planetary energy needs. One way to do this is to use nano-engineered solar panels and fuel cells. Another, slightly crazier technique to generate massive amounts of clean and renewable energy might be Space-Based Solar Power or Space Solar Power (SBSP or SSP). Space effectively consists of nothing but energy, so surely we can capture a little bit for ourselves?

> **❛Science has not yet mastered prophecy. We predict too much for the next year and yet far too little for the next ten.❜**
>
> **Neil Armstrong, test pilot and astronaut (1969)**

Harnessing the Sun's power How on Earth could this work? The idea goes back to the late 1960s and early 1970s. After all, we've recently figured out how to broadcast electricity through the air via wireless technology, so to some extent this idea is a logical progression. And don't forget that we already beam phone calls and TV signals from satellites to Earth using electromagnetic frequencies, so why not power?

Space-based power generation has some considerable advantages over Earth-based systems too. In space there's effectively no weather, so, for

timeline

1913	1950s	1964	1971
US patent for a solar cell	Bell Labs develop solar cells to aid space exploration	*Direct Use of the Sun's Energy* published by Farrington Daniels	Salyut 1 space flight powered by solar cells

instance, there are no clouds to obstruct the Sun, and collecting dishes could receive solar radiation most of the time, rather than being restricted to daylight hours. There's no air in space either, so the solar radiation is not being filtered by atmospheric gases. And the system produces no pollution.

Putting collecting dishes into space would obviously be a mammoth task, but we have done it already on a very small scale. There's also the issue of maintenance. Space is not a benign environment, and equipment will get damaged from rocks and manmade space junk, so how will we repair it? Robots permanently stationed in space probably. Likewise how can we beam the energy back to Earth without losing energy in transmission?

There's the difficulty of keeping the space-based energy beams locked onto the rectifying antennas (or rectennas) connected to the receiving stations

Patent #3,781,647

In 1973, US Patent number 3,781,647 was granted to Mr Peter Glaser, a Vice President of Arthur D. Little, a management consulting company, for a way of transmitting power over large distances, namely from space to the Earth's surface, using microwaves. One year later, NASA studied the idea and said that it suffered from a few problems, most notably cost, but nevertheless concluded that the idea was promising. Throughout the remainder of the 1970s and into the 1980s other studies were commissioned, but the overall feeling was that, while interesting, the concept was high risk both in terms of cost and environmental impact. However, in 1999, NASA established the Space Solar Power Exploratory Research and Technology Program (SERT) to continue investigations.

1979	2029	2040	2070
Jimmy Carter puts solar panels on the White House	Tests begin on new solar-based collection dishes	First test of space-to-Earth solar power transmission	Earth-based technology breakthrough makes SBSP redundant

❝Why would anyone be interested in space-based solar power when commercial utility scale solar technology on the ground today costs 0.3 per cent of its price?❞

Energy & Capital.com

back on Earth. But the history of technology suggests that these, and other problems, are merely a matter of time and money, especially money in this case.

In 2009, Pacific Gas & Electric (a major energy utility in the USA) stated that it was seeking to develop a relationship with a company called Solaren Corporation ultimately to buy solar energy beamed from space via satellites that will be operating commercially from the year 2016. Or how about the American and Japanese scientists who successfully transmitted energy in the form of microwaves between two Hawaiian Islands 145km (90 miles) apart a few years ago? It's even theoretically possible that if we build space elevators (see Chapter 39) between our planet and near space, we could use these physical structures to host some wiring, which might be used to transmit energy Earthwards. Or maybe we'll develop batteries so powerful that it's simply a matter of harvesting the Sun in space, storing it in big batteries, then sending vehicles into space to bring the batteries back to Earth.

Looking at the alternatives Cynics may point to the difficulties relating to regulation and licensing of space-based solar power. Currently the United Nations would have to approve any such technology, but some nations may seek to block it on the grounds of national security. Turning beams of energy into death rays is a bit far-fetched, but if instead of using microwaves we used lasers based on the Moon, this might make a few insecure nations rather anxious.

Other cynical observers might point out that the concept of solar energy from space is mind-blowingly stupid, especially when you stop to consider the huge impact that billions of highly efficient next-generation solar panels on every single roof, vehicle or alongside every road on our planet

Fact follows fiction

In one episode of the Japanese animation series *Mobile Suit Gundam*, set in 2037, mankind turns to solar-based power to escape from various Earth-bound energy conflicts. As is often the case, fact follows fiction and Japanese scientists are now working on ways to do this for real. The plan, which is being developed by Japan's space agency, the Japan Aerospace Exploration Agency (JAXA), is to have a working prototype built by the year 2030 that will generate 1 gigawatt of power – roughly what a Japanese nuclear power plant produces.

could deliver instead. We could potentially turn almost every window or flat surface that faced outwards into a solar collection point and build giant solar collection factories in deserts, thereby creating a new generation of energy-producing nations (See Chapter 7).

We could also float solar panels on reservoirs, dams and lakes (thereby reducing the growth of unwanted algae). This last idea might appeal especially to farmers or water companies because it would instantly turn one revenue stream into two. Add all of these ideas together and we would generate a staggering amount of power with almost no down side, especially when considered against the cost of doing something similar from space. Then again, it's precisely the difficult and audacious nature of producing solar energy from space that will, one assumes, appeal to the average technology entrepreneur with big dreams and access to a few trillion dollars.

the condensed idea
Beaming energy from space

38 Moon mining

The Moon offers numerous intriguing possibilities. Space hotels and permanent space outposts are two ideas that have long captured the imagination. Hosting space-based energy relay stations or weapons are others. But the most likely and practical possibility is mining the Moon for rare minerals and other much-needed natural resources.

The first Moon mine effectively began in December 1972 when an astronaut called Harrison Schmitt from the last manned mission to the Moon, Apollo 17, collected 110kg (244lb) of Moon rocks and brought them back to Earth. Not much has happened on the Moon since, but back on Earth we've invented various new devices reliant on what are known as 'rare earth minerals'. These inventions include consumer electronics such as iPads to bits of industrial machinery like wind turbines.

A rare earth mineral is literally one that is very rare on Earth. Helium-3 is rare on our planet, but was found in soil samples from the Apollo 17 mission to the Moon. It's related to the gas that's often used to blow up balloons, but that's not why it's interesting. Helium-3 has one fairly unusual characteristic, which makes it ideal for a new and highly efficient form of nuclear fusion. It could solve most, if not all, of our energy problems on Earth, not least because Helium-3 reactors are less complex than conventional nuclear reactors and create zero radioactive waste. The Moon's surface may be littered with Helium-3. That's because Helium originates from the Sun, but Helium-3 rarely makes it to our planet because the Earth's magnetic field pushes the solar winds that contain it back towards the Moon and the other planets.

timeline

2018	2039	2042	2060
Large-scale seabed mining begins	Seabed largely exhausted of useful materials	India, Russia and China start Moon mine trials	India and China engage in Moon-based conflict over resource extraction

A source of conflict ... The idea of mining the Moon is related to Alt.Space (Chapter 36) in the sense that it's highly likely that private-sector entrepreneurs, rather than government agencies, will be the first to establish whether or not there's money to be made on or beneath the Moon's surface. And to get there, space entrepreneurs need cheap flights. They will probably also need power once they're on the Moon and some smart machines, or robots, to do the work once there. Some space entrepreneurs may decide that the Moon is a good environment for manufacturing as well. The existence of abundant supplies of hydrogen may, for instance, make it far cheaper to manufacture or refine rocket fuel on the Moon than back on Earth.

> **I suppose we shall soon travel by air-vessels; make air instead of sea voyages; and at length find our way to the Moon, in spite of the want of atmosphere.**
>
> Lord Byron,
> poet, 1822

Rare here, not elsewhere

China's tightening grip on supplies of rare earths means the hunt is on for alternatives. One idea is rock-eating bacteria, such as *Leptospirillum*, which occur naturally in some of the most inhospitable environments. They get their energy from chemical reactions with sulphides and can therefore hasten the breakdown of certain minerals. Some base metals, ranging from copper and zinc to gold and uranium, occur as sulphides. Historically, it's been rather costly to get these metals out of the ground, but this could be about to change. A project set up in Finland has found that nickel, zinc, copper, lead, tin, gold, cobalt, rhenium, selenium, platinum, palladium and uranium can all be extracted from rocks using nothing but bacteria.

2070
New method of extracting minerals from seawater makes Moon mines redundant

2090
Abundant amounts of gemstones found on Mars

2100
Fresh water found beneath Moon's surface triggers 'water rush'

> **❛I think that the Moon will be treated no differently than the international waters in our oceans ... in this case no one really owns the water but any company or country can mine the resources.❜**
>
> Naveen Jain, co-founder of MoonEx

Quite how the international community will view such developments is anyone's guess. In theory the Moon is simply a big rock waiting to be exploited just like any other. Although current space law (dating from 1967) states that nobody can own any part of the Moon, which would presumably include materials found there. Rather oddly, however, the treaty also permits the exploitation of resources found in outer space 'without interference'.

Some of the largest fortunes on Earth have been made and continue to be created by drilling or digging large holes in the ground to extract precious resources, and there's no reason to suppose that future fortunes won't be made doing much the same thing out in space. Throughout history mankind has explored and colonized new lands and extracted materials that people thought were of value at the time. In a sense, the Moon, or other planets, may be no different. But some nations may not agree.

Or an answer to our problems? The Moon may be viewed as a strategic asset, either in terms of its location (easy death-ray distance to Earth) or perhaps because it contains large quantities of raw materials urgently needed back on Earth. George Friedman, author of *The Next 100 Years* and founder and CEO of Stratfor, for example, sees the development of US Space Forces, an arm of the military quite separate from the US Air Force. He also believes that the US military will underwrite much of the cost of developing space-based solar power (Chapter 37) because it could solve the issue of supplying electricity to battlefield troops and robotic systems back on Earth.

The Moon may represent the next frontier in terms of resources, bringing with it low-cost flights and permanent Moon colonies. A peaceful and abundant future that science-fiction writers and moviemakers have imagined for many years. Conversely, the Moon may represent a dangerous new frontier, where increasingly desperate nations, eager to secure energy security for their own people, battle it out with other nations to survive.

Extrapolating again?

The argument that we're running out of much-needed minerals and other key resources seems fairly solid, but it's quite possible that we're doing what we often do – extrapolating, either from present conditions or past experience. At the moment we need certain resources, but in the future perhaps our need won't be so great because we'll have invented something totally new that's dependent upon something else entirely, perhaps some substance that's in abundant supply.

Or perhaps there's a third, slightly weirder Moon future. In the film *Moon*, made by Duncan Jones (also known as Zowie Bowie), Sam Bell is the sole Moon-based employee of Lunar Industries and his job is to oversee the cosmic quarrying of Helium-3 by various automated harvesting machines. The Helium-3 is required back on Earth to generate clean energy. Sam's only companion is an AI assistant and soon things start to go rather wrong.

This is science fiction, but it's not too much of a mind-stretch to imagine something similar happening in real life. That we'll one day set up a mining station on the Moon and start to transport much-needed resources back to Earth. This could trigger not only a new form of international diplomacy and conflict, but some very real and very strange relationships between human beings and machines a long way from home.

the condensed idea
Using the Moon like any big rock

39 Space elevators

Imagine a beanstalk 10,000km (6,200 miles) long extending into space, connected to a counterweight 35,790km (22,200 miles) up, and you have roughly what's known as a space elevator. It may seem like science fiction, but researchers are working on it. A space elevator could be used to slingshot materials, perhaps people, into space without the need for rockets or rocket fuel.

This idea is already being explored. The Japanese held a competition in 2009 to see who could use space tether-type technology (aka, a space ladder, sky hook, space lift or geostationary orbital tether) to hoist their climbers the fastest. A German machine climbed the 150m (500ft) in 52 seconds. In America, a US foundation has been holding annual competitions to win a $1 million dollar prize, where a climber (currently a machine carrying a payload rather than an actual person) has to pull itself up a distance of 1km (0.6 miles).

The ultimate problem here, of course, is that no material has ever been strong enough to create a fixed structure of the necessary length. But the discovery of carbon nanotubes (CNTs) in 1991 has possibly changed this. Scientists say they still need a mass-production system for carbon materials and a rapid-speed propulsion system, but this may now be solved, following the breakthrough development of graphene, potentially the world's strongest material. This is essentially a honeycomb lattice (or atomic-scale chicken wire if you prefer) that contains carbon atoms in hexagons almost as tough as CNTs. US researchers say that a working elevator could be built as early as 2030, as long as someone is willing to spend the $10 billion needed for the hypothetical mega-engineering project to get off the ground.

timeline

1895	1959	1966	1975
Konstantin Tsiolkovsky suggests the idea of a giant tower reaching to space	Yuri Artsutanov suggests dropping a tether down from an orbiting satellite	Bachus, Isaacs, Vine and Bradner propose a 'Sky-hook' device	Jerome Pearson suggests a tapering tether

Going up?

The idea of riding an elevator into space is not as crazy as it sounds. Indeed, if you go back a few hundred years the notion of using any kind of elevator rather than stairs would have seemed somewhat fanciful. Even after lifts had been invented, the idea of using a fully automated version without a human operator would have been regarded as positively dangerous. A working space elevator is obviously still a long way off, but one current plan consists of a 50km (30 mile) base station much like a very large Eiffel Tower with a very long cable extending into inner space. Pods or vehicles powered by electromagnetic force would then be propelled up and down the cable to an orbiting space station.

Space logistics Why would anyone want to do this? Partly because the challenge is there, but a space elevator could also drastically reduce the cost of space freight. For example, communication satellites could be delivered into space more easily, repair robots could be dispatched to fix broken solar energy-collection dishes, and Moon rocks could be transported back to Earth on regular freight shuttles. Space logistics essentially. Moreover, if anyone ever came up with a better idea, this whole space supply chain or transport system could all be easily dismantled, no permanent damage done. Another thought: perhaps if we built long-enough wires, we could put them into another plant's magnetic field to create a giant dynamo.

Could any of this really happen? One problem is that parts of the wire – or whatever you call it – that's located close to the Earth will be travelling much

> **If the laws of celestial mechanics make it possible for an object to stay fixed in the sky, might it not be possible to lower a cable down to the surface – and so to establish an elevator system?**
> **Arthur C. Clarke, sci-fi author**

1979	2003	2011	2070
A space elevator appears in an Arthur C. Clarke novel	Liftport Group is formed to develop space elevators	First European Space Elevator challenge takes place	Japanese scientists claim to have developed a working elevator

slower than parts of the wire higher up. This is something known as the Coriolis Effect. Imagine placing a small and relatively light object on a large disc that's spinning at a constant speed (an old 33rpm vinyl album by the Rolling Stones on a record player might be a good, if somewhat obsolete, example).

If you place the object near the middle of the disc, it will stay there. But if you move the object to the edge of the disc it should be thrown off, not because the disc is spinning at more than 33 revolutions per minute, but because the outer edges of the disc have a greater circumference and the disc needs to travel faster to remain at 33 revolutions per minute. But if you throw a cable up into space – or drop one down to Earth – there will be a huge drag at the lower end, which could cause the whole thing to jiggle about and possibly break free. It's enough to make anyone's head spin.

Issues abound Another issue might once again be the strategic implications of such a radical technology, especially if the idea was practical, replicable and reliable, and nations started to argue with each other over its use. If a relatively independent organization, such as the United Nations, built such elevators, there would, no doubt, be lots of squabbling over who gets to use it first, and how access is allocated. This alone could keep the elevator stuck firmly on the ground floor for years.

Audacious and outrageous predictions

History often repeats itself, but so too does the future – especially when science fiction predicts the shape of things to come, as it sometimes does. It hasn't come to pass yet, but in 1979, Arthur C. Clarke published a sci-fi novel called *The Fountains of Paradise*, which features an engineer called Dr Vannevar Morgan. Dr Morgan has the brilliant if somewhat radical idea of building a 32,000km (roughly 22,000 mile) orbital tower from the ground of one planet to the base of a mountain on another.

But if the technology were to be developed by a single nation, or a private company, the arguments could turn really nasty, especially if access to the elevator gave a serious strategic advantage in terms of obtaining much-needed rare resources or deploying space-based weapons.

And what if, by the time the elevator was built, conditions on Earth had seriously deteriorated due to climate change or perhaps due to the proliferation of malicious robotic replicants? This could, in turn, create a very long queue for a one-ride-only ticket (on what could, by this time, possibly be known as 'The Ark') and 'queue rage' would develop fairly rapidly. Perhaps we'd solve this by allocating tickets by birthday date (see the movie *Contagion*) or ability to pay – thereby creating instant societal polarization and resentment.

As a result of this, and other serious problems, don't expect to see any true space elevators any time soon, although if anyone does one day manage to perfect this technology, things could get really quite fantastic. One commentator has already come up with the idea of throwing a long and very strong rope out into space to capture small asteroids and haul them back to Earth to mine them for Helium-3. Don't hold your breath about this idea, though. This, and ideas related to it, are likely to stay firmly rooted in science fiction for quite a while yet.

> **This is no longer science fiction ... we came out of the workshop saying, "We may very well be able to do this."**
> **David Smitherman, NASA**

the condensed idea
Jack and the Beanstalk goes sci-fi

40 Alien intelligence

Have you ever wondered what would happen if scientists discovered compelling evidence of intelligent life existing on another planet? Or how we'd respond to an intelligent civilization that decided to pay us a visit in person? Believe it or not, some sensible people at SETI – an organization dedicated to finding other forms of intelligent life out in space – have been thinking about this.

The SETI (Search for Extraterrestrial Intelligence) Institute is a fascinating organization full of hugely intelligent and ferociously curious people. Their job is to find out whether or not there is intelligent life on other planets, which, as Arthur C. Clarke once pointed out, is one of the most fascinating and important questions that we can ask.

But what would happen if the scientists at SETI actually found something? Would they tell us? According to Seth Shostak, Senior Astronomer at SETI, the news would almost certainly leak out. And what if SETI picked up a radio communication from a planet far, far away and the communication was a message? What if 'they' were heading here? I would imagine that the answer would be a mixture of panic, on a level never previously seen, and bewildered, astonished wonderment and joy. Aliens are clearly fertile territory for conspiracy theorists and other assorted fringe thinkers. But it seems reasonable to assume that a genuine communication from a highly intelligent life form, somewhere else in the galaxy, would have extraordinary effects on things back on Earth.

timeline

1855	1960	1977	1995
First exoplanet false alarm	Drake equation	'Wow!' Signal (a radio signal picked up by SETI in 1977)	Discovery of 51 Pegasi b, an orbiting planet

What are SETI and others doing to find evidence of extraterrestrial life? The answer, at the moment, is to look for obvious signals created by radio or optical transmissions, produced either by individual planets or by broad areas of space, but the field is developing rapidly due to advances in technology.

Drake and Fermi But what is the likelihood of finding intelligent life elsewhere (or of intelligent life elsewhere finding us)? If we're talking about the search for life, and better still intelligent life on other planets, reference should be made to the Drake Equation, which attempts to estimate how many intelligent civilizations might exist in our own galaxy, namely the Milky Way. The equation is named after Frank Drake and essentially says that the answer is somewhere between zero and 182 million depending upon the rate of star formation, the percentage of stars that have planets, the number of planets that might support life, the number that create intelligent life, the number that broadcast their presence and how long such broadcasts create

> **All civilizations become either spacefaring or extinct.**
>
> **Carl Sagan,** *Pale Blue Dot: A Vision of the Human Future in Space,* 1994.

Post-detection protocol

What's the official protocol if the folks at SETI find what they think is a sign of intelligent life elsewhere in the universe? The first step, in theory, is that SETI's funders would be secretly informed. Given that NASA currently funds astrobiology research through SETI, this might mean that SETI would inform the executive government of the United States, which means the US President. SETI would then seek to confirm the signal before looking for external and independent verification. If the communication were proven to be real, a telegram (not an email or SMS) would then be sent to the Central Bureau for Astronomical Telegrams, then there would be a press conference. At least that's the theory.

2001	**2012**	**2036**	**2066**
Exoplanet HD 28185b found in habitable zone	Discovery that exoplanet GJ 1214b is covered in water	Evidence found that life on Earth started in space	First contact with alien life form (it's not where we expect)

> **❝For I dipt into the future, far as human eye could see,**
> **Saw the vision of the world, and all the wonder that would be;**
> **Saw the heavens fill with commerce, argosies of magic sails ...❞**

Alfred, Lord Tennyson, *Locksley Hall*, 1842

detectable signals. But remember: this number above relates only to our own galaxy and there could even be as many as 500 billion other galaxies out there.

Second, and perhaps more importantly, we need to consider the Fermi Paradox. Enrico Fermi was an Italian scientist who came up with a simple idea concerning intelligent life on other planets. Namely, that while the sheer size and ancient age of the known universe implies that other intelligent and technologically advanced life forms exist, there has never been any observable evidence that they do. So where are they? The answer could either be that 'they' are not in fact out 'there', or that we're looking for them in all the wrong places – or possibly for the wrong type of intelligence. Perhaps there is plenty of intelligent life out there in the universe, but it's not intelligent life as we know it here on Earth.

Or maybe life is abundant on other planets, but intelligent life is extremely rare, so rare in fact that we might be far better employed properly looking after our fellow human beings and other forms of life back here on Earth rather than looking for new forms of life, intelligent or otherwise, in the far-flung corners of the known universe.

Taking action This thought links to another interesting theory, which states that as intelligence evolves on a planet, the dominant species either exhausts all of the available resources or they develop highly advanced and hugely deadly weapons (possibly to fight wars to obtain rare resources), which eventually leads to their extinction. In other words, perhaps there was intelligent life elsewhere in the universe once, but it was all wiped out long ago, and we are all that remains.

Bringing Arthur C. Clarke back into the alien equation, he also famously said that when it comes to the question of whether or not we are alone there are only two possible answers. Either the answer is 'no', which is a fairly terrifying thought, or the answer is 'yes', which is equally terrifying. Personally, I think that both answers could be regarded as something of a call to arms (no military implications intended).

If we are alone then we should start to take more care of our fellow human beings and properly look after the tiny fragile planet that we call home. If we're not alone, then we should do exactly the same thing and hope that 'they' are sufficiently friendly and altruistic. As for whether we'll one day find evidence of intelligence life elsewhere, my view would be yes, partly because of the sheer number of planets out there and partly because there could be other universes or dimensions currently hidden from human awareness. This takes us to the fringes of physics and into mainstream science fiction, but, as we've seen, the two can collide. What if, for instance, space was infinite? Could this mean an infinite number of permutations of matter? This idea is a bit of a stretch, partly because there's a difference between a situation where everything must happen and one where anything could happen. Nevertheless, it's an interesting thought that you may not be the only you. Aliens among us indeed.

Why do people see UFOs?

The Australian futurist Richard Neville once turned the tables on the likes of SETI by asking not whether UFOs are real, but why people keep seeing them? Some UFO spotters and alien abductees are clearly deluded, but some are otherwise sensible. So what's it all about? I suspect the answer has something to do with a desire for magic in a rational and scientific age. We would like to believe in something much bigger than ourselves too.

the condensed idea
Are we alone?

41 Mobile radiation

There are more than 5 billion mobile phones on the planet, plus countless other mobile devices connected to wireless networks. Mobiles, in particular, have become a ubiquitous presence, with many users literally addicted to them. But what if the radiation from such devices was seriously harmful to human health? What if mobile devices were killing us?

Mobile (cell) phones create what's known as radiofrequency energy, a type of non-ionizing, or low-frequency, electromagnetic radiation. In theory this is totally safe, despite the fact that human cells, tissues and organs closest to where a phone is used or carried absorb this radiation. But imagine, for a moment, that these devices were not safe. Indeed, imagine the consequences if long-term or heavy mobile phone use included the development of malignant brain tumours or other forms of cancer? Given the ubiquity of these devices and the fact that use is highest within relatively young segments of any population, the implications would be devastating. Wi-Fi hotspots, wireless phones and 'electronic smog' created by everything from power lines to 'broadcast' electricity for wireless (cable-free) homes and offices could be doing much the same thing.

If you read the fine print with your Blackberry, you'll discover that it should be held at least 2.5cm (1in) from your head. Apple recommends 1.5cm (0.6in) for its iPhone. Considering Americans chat on their phones for 2.26 trillion minutes annually, it would be interesting to get a ruler out.

timeline

2011	2012	2013	2016
Expert studying EMF radiation found to be lobbyist for the mobile industry	Mass hysteria caused by text messages about the Mayan calendar	Phone-spam and viruses start to become a problem	Reported cases of brain tumours among 8–18-year-olds treble in 18 months

Information pandemics

We are moving towards a brave, but increasingly strange, new world. For example, why was bird flu scarier when it was elsewhere (in Asia and Continental Europe) than when it actually arrived in Britain for the first time? The answer, it seems, is that anxiety has taken over from optimism as the dominant cultural force. Consequently, we run from one supposed threat to another without stopping to think about the actual level of threat posed. Our newfound connectivity also means that information about threats spreads like wildfire, so what could once be contained and sensibly analysed now spreads before we have time to assess the real risk. It's as though we've collectively lost our critical faculties. We feel that we're vulnerable and at risk to forces beyond our control. But we also feel that humanity is itself destructive so we end up fearing ourselves. And if it's not bird flu, it's climate change, terrorism, volancoes, earthquakes and EMF radiation from mobile phones ...

Radiation risks Dr Devra Davis from the University of Pittsburgh, the author of *Disconnect*, says that incidences of brain cancer have not gone up since mobiles were first introduced around twenty years ago. But the average obscures the frightening increase among 20–29-year-olds. Children are particularly vulnerable because radiation penetrates more deeply into their brain than in adults. According to Dr Davis, children are more susceptible to radiation because their skulls are thinner and their brains are still developing.

> **'Forty per cent of cells taken from mobile phone users show DNA damage.'**
>
> *Indian Journal of Human Genetics*

A recent Swedish study of 1,200 people diagnosed with malignant brain tumours in 1997–2003 analysed their mobile and cordless phone use. People who started using mobiles as teenagers, and continued to use them for ten years, were 4.9 times more likely to get malignant brain tumours. For cordless phone users over ten years, the risk was 3.9 times.

2017	2018	2022	2058
Government mandates introduction of Wi-Fi 'coldspots'	Decline in voice communication slows spread of problems	People start to implant 'safe' phones inside their heads	Class actions in USA and China against telcos and computer firms

"The greatest polluting element in the Earth's environment is the proliferation of electromagnetic fields. I consider that to be a far greater threat on a global scale than warming, or the increase of chemical elements in the environment."

Dr Robert Becker, Nobel nominee and EMF radiation pioneer

Yet mobiles have become the new cuddly toys for kids, sometimes for kids as young as seven. Some countries take the risks seriously. In France, it is illegal to market mobiles to children under 12 and they can't use them in primary schools; other countries, including the UK, merely discourage phone use with very limited success.

Radiation, or radiofrequency, exposure is measured as the specific absorption rate (SAR). This should be no more than 1.6 watts per kilogram. San Francisco has passed an ordnance that forces manufacturers to declare their SARs so that consumers can make an informed decision. Naturally, the industry trade group, CTIA – The Wireless Association – claims that all Federal Communications Commission-approved phones are safe.

None of the results from mobile phone studies is yet conclusive. While the experts are still arguing about radiation from mobiles, you can wear wired headsets, speakers, or use texting to protect your head. If one day mobiles are proved to be carcinogenic, phone makers, network operators and even computer companies could become the new tobacco companies, but on an even greater scale. And the damage may not be limited to carcinogenic effects either. According to Professor Olle Johansson, a neuroscientist at the Karolinska Institute in Stockholm, other effects of heavy or long-term mobile use could include serious sleep disturbance, genetic damage and even learning difficulties.

More use, not less It's highly likely that mobile phones and tablet computers with wireless Internet connectivity will be among our most heavily used devices, owned by most people around the world, in the future. We will use them to access almost everything, including other people, due to their low cost and above all their convenience. Knowing what we do about human behaviour, though, few of us, and few institutions, will have much of a backup plan if such devices are declared unequivocally unsafe.

No smoking gun

People who've been using mobile phones for less than ten years appear to be safe from any likelihood of cancer. But an international Interphone study into whether mobile phones increase cancer rates has been unable to assess longer-term use simply because people cannot recall that far back. Not only that, phones from more than ten years ago were considerably different from those today. Some cancer experts have publicly warned that there's enough evidence to suggest an increase in head tumours, but the International Commission on Non-Ionizing Radiation Protection says the longer-term results are not likely to be available for some time. In some ways, this is a repeat of the numerous studies into tobacco use. They warned that tobacco was addictive and dangerous, yet people continued to smoke and the tobacco companies continued to sell cigarettes. Many people are now addicted to mobiles and it seems unlikely they'll change their habits without good evidence.

If our mobile phones were proved to be mass killers, you'd think that we'd probably stop using them pretty fast, but evidence from smoking, overeating and alcohol abuse studies might suggest otherwise. We'll probably just ignore the research and carry on as usual.

If, however, we did suddenly stop using them, or at least stopped trusting them, the impact would be catastrophic. It's bad enough already when our email goes down or a mobile gets lost for 30 minutes, so imagine the reaction if wireless devices were unusable for months or years. We'd eventually recover. Initially we might start reinstalling fixed-line (wired) telephones and other fixed-line devices, but market mechanisms would quickly kick in, responding rapidly to demand and encouraging invention. At least that's the theory.

the condensed idea
A potential killer
under our noses

42 Biohazards & plagues

One commonly imagined future is essentially utopian. It is metallic and supersmart, full of shiny new objects, robots, flying cars, space suits and dinner in a pill. But there are also more dystopian futures, especially those featuring a repeat of the Black Death that finished off around a third of Europe's population or a sequel to the flu pandemic of 1918–19 that killed between 20 and 40 million people.

It strikes me as odd that we assume that life will go on, more or less as it has always done. But 'always' is often a contemporary concept. We generally compare the present to the relatively recent past. The same tends to be true of the future: we often assume that the near future will be a logical or familiar extension of present conditions. Therefore, we do not take into account, for example, the Spanish Inquisition or the American Civil War. Even World Wars One and Two, which are relatively recent, are generally forgotten by many, at least in terms of the numbers killed (around 70 million men, women and children) or the general day-to-day conditions. It is as though modern life is programming us constantly to forget. The rapid flow of news and the daily deluge of data mean that our focus is increasingly on now and the next few days. We do not generally prepare for the far future any more than we consider the distant past.

A dark future? So what new doomsday scenarios are there out there? It's potentially a long list. We have two main problems. First, more of us are living closer together in crowded cities and moving around faster in an interconnected world thanks to various regulations and innovations

timeline

1918–19	1981	1986	1995
Great flu pandemic kills 20–40 million people	HIV (Human Immunodeficiency Virus) identified (25 million killed to date)	BSE linked to new variant of Creutzfeldt-Jakob disease in human beings	Sarin gas attacks in Japan

in economics, transport and infrastructure. Our animals live closer together – and closer to us some people might argue – so when a naturally occurring pathogen does break out it travels much farther, and has the potential to travel much faster between species than before. This lack of physical containment goes some way to explaining the recent outbreaks of the H5N1 influenza virus, SARS, Dengue and Ebola, all of which originated in animals and were then rapidly spread by human beings.

The second problem is technology. New technologies are emerging faster than before. Many are quite powerful and some can be used for bad as well as good ends. Genetics, which makes it possible to create new micro-organisms, is a case in point. Most of the time, genetics will be used for entirely peaceful purposes. But there is no reason why some day someone won't utilize the science for something more sinister. Again, this has happened already. Smallpox and anthrax have been used as weapons before and in 1995 we had sarin gas attacks on the Tokyo subway system. So could an evil mind create a new deadly micro-organism that is lethal only to a specific race or ethnicity? Racism, stealth and deniability all rolled into one tiny and easily transportable package?

Return of the old

Many of the countries most at risk of disease are those least prepared to spot them. These are places of rapid population growth, agricultural and industrial changes, deforestation, heavy use of antibiotics, and areas where there is contact with diseased animals. Nigeria and India are both high risk. As a result of these and other risk factors, there is evidence that some old diseases – plague, rickets, and tuberculosis – are on the rise again. The World Health Organization reports 1,000–3,000 plague cases a year, carried by rodents, mostly in Africa. Tuberculosis is more likely to be brought in by African or Indian immigrants who then live in poor and deprived areas where resistance to disease is lower.

> **❝For now, we will have to live in a world where a relatively minor flu outbreak in Mexico City can send markets reeling in Tokyo.❞**
>
> **Warwick McKibbin, the Lowry Institute**

2002	2012	2020	2049
SARS outbreak begins (named SARS in 2003)	A typical year for the common flu (3,000–5,000 killed in the USA)	People in Britain still say 'bless you' when someone sneezes (a reference to the Black Death)	HI48B virus kills 500,000

❝Dr Jeremy Stone: "...with this new knowledge, there is no guarantee that another so-called 'biological crisis' won't occur again."
Senator: "Hmm. What do we do about that?"
Dr Jeremy Stone: "Precisely, Senator. What do we do?"❞

Closing lines from *The Andromeda Strain* (1971)

What would be the consequences? Apart from an outbreak of fear, any major pandemic would create a need for mass disposal of bodies. Many of the ideas we cherish – such as saying goodbye to loved ones, or being able to visit their graves – might vanish into plague pits alongside national sovereignty and human rights. We could be transported back to Europe at the time of the Black Death in 1348, at least in the early days. There are also the economic effects. Work done by Warwick McKibbin at the Lowry Institute in Sydney (quoted in *The Doomsday Handbook* by Alok Jha) suggests that even a mild repeat of the 1918 flu pandemic would kill almost 1.5 million people and would reduce economic output by $330 billion (in 2006 prices).

A bigger outbreak might kill 142 million and shrink output in some economies by as much as 50 per cent. Or perhaps it's more prosaic than that: Type 2 diabetes? Maybe hundreds of millions will die, simply because they eat too much and don't exercise their bodies enough. As for biotech disasters, the potential for serious accidents is significant. What if poor synthetic biology regulation leads to people taking shortcuts, creating a new form of bug that can't be killed using any known techniques? The bug might not be a direct human threat, but if it destroyed the world's wheat, maize or rice crop, the result could be mass starvation in particular regions.

Side issues Problems may occur due to a combination of factors. What if global demand for meat created a pressing need to dispose of animal carcasses? This could mean illegal dumping, which might cause a growth in feral dogs in some parts of the world, which could lead to a massive increase in cases of rabies. Or what if a global economic boom

What if?

What would happen if there were a real pandemic? Forget how many people might die, this has been debated, well, to death. What about some of the more mundane consequences? Once people started to die in serious numbers, we would want to avoid other people. We would stop travelling to work, preferring to work from home. Schools would be closed and so would physical shops. Food would become a serious problem and stockpiling and stealing of food would rise dramatically. Money might become an issue too, as people wouldn't want to physically touch cash that had been touched by somebody else.

meant more people were building swimming pools, but the boom was followed by a bust and the homes were repossessed then left empty? Stagnant water in swimming pools, in combination with warmer weather caused by climate change, could lead to outbreaks of malaria in North America and Europe.

We should remain open-minded and vigilant about various future possibilities. Nevertheless, we should face up to the fact that bad things happen and we cannot be prepared for everything. We cannot, after all, prepare for events that we can't even imagine. The good news is that, with very few exceptions, life will go on no matter what. We are resilient. We adapt. Or perhaps not, which could prove to be the biggest disaster of all.

the condensed idea
Bad things can
happen biologically

43 Nuclear terrorism

Nuclear weapons have been around for more than half a century and have been used offensively twice. Both occasions involved a nation that was officially at war with another. The chance of a sovereign country attacking another with nuclear weapons has probably declined of late. On the other hand, the probability of a non-state actor using a nuclear device has probably risen.

Let's get one thing sorted out straight away. It's not easy to launch an attack with a nuclear weapon unless you are one of the eight nations that officially possess such a device. China launching a nuclear attack on the USA, or vice versa, is not impossible, but it's not very probable either. India versus Pakistan or Israel versus Iran represent a more serious nuclear threat, but even here the probability remains relatively low.

From possible to probable So what else might happen? One popular scenario is a terrorist group using a nuclear weapon hidden inside a suitcase. This idea flowed from reports in the USA in the 1960s that the Russians had developed a number of small portable nuclear devices. Whether this is true or not is still unclear, but according to Russian defector Stanislav Lunev, writing in 1998, Russian-made 'suitcase nukes' are hidden in the USA for potential use in any future conflict.

Terrorists getting hold of these devices or developing their own suitcase or backpack device wouldn't be easy, or cheap, but it's certainly not completely impossible either. You wouldn't even need a large suitcase.

timeline

1995	2010	2018	2022
Terrorists attempt to detonate dirty bomb in Moscow	Stuxnet virus attacks nuclear facilities in Iran	Man arrested after attempting to sell radioactive materials on eBay	Al-Qaeda attempts to detonate dirty devices on three subway systems

A market for everything

Terrorism and disaster are among the fastest-growing areas of study in the USA, with more than 100 colleges and universities developing courses along the lines of 'Terrorism and Apocalyptic Violence'. Partly funded by the Department of Homeland Security, the new courses are intended to educate government officials and other managers about various first-response aspects of terrorism including crowd control, public health and dealing with the press.

More likely is something less devastating, but equally frightening, especially if your aim is to destroy the hearts and minds of politicians and instil a sense of panic in the general public. If your objective is fear, there are many opportunities open to you, and a bomber – or bomb – will eventually get through. For example, imagine the panic that would grip North America if someone – and it could easily be a US national – did manage to set off a nuclear device in Times Square. The physical damage wouldn't need to be especially large.

Clearly, it's not the intention here to write a handbook for terrorists, but let's stop to consider a few of the relatively well-known events that could, and probably will, happen in the not too distant future.

Dirty bombs et al A 'dirty bomb' is the term used to describe a conventional explosive device that also contains radioactive material. The power of the conventional explosion essentially vaporizes the radioactive material, which is then spread over a small area by the force of the blast. If it's windy, the wind may then distribute the effects over a much wider area. And such a device can be put in a suitcase. Getting hold of materials such as strontium-90 and caesium-137 isn't

> **❛Nuclear terrorism is the gravest danger we face.❜**
> **Barack Obama, 2008 US Presidential Campaign**

2030	2060	2080
Tactical nuclear weapons used in Georgia	25 per cent of nations found to have secret nuclear programmes	Nuclear development abandoned in favour of dark-matter weapons

easy. But given the collapse of the former Soviet Union, the chaos and corruption in states such as Pakistan, the right contacts and a large enough amount of money, means that it's not totally impossible. You can even obtain small amounts of dangerous material from your local hospital.

According to an International Atomic Energy Agency (IAEA) report, most major nations in the world hold some kind of radioactive material, and around 100 nations have weak or non-existent controls to stop the stealing of these materials.

A dirty bomb is not a weapon of mass destruction, but it is a weapon of mass distraction and disruption. Given the right payload, such a device could cause serious damage to the centre of a major city and the anxiety it created would be considerable, having long-lasting effects, not least because you cannot see or smell the radioactive dust. We have had an accidental taste of this before too. The nuclear accident at Chernobyl in 1986 is perhaps one instance. Fukushima in 2011 is possibly another.

When, not if?

A dirty bomb in a major city would inflict massive psychological damage. As for the use of a conventional nuclear weapon by a terrorist group, this is technically much more difficult and more likely to be delivered by a rogue state or deranged dictator. How might a democratic government respond to such an incident? Assuming that a culprit could be identified, retaliation would probably be fairly instant and severe. But even if tens of millions of people died, life would eventually return to something approaching normal – as anyone living near Hiroshima or Nagasaki might testify. This seems almost inconceivable, but there is something remarkably resilient about the human race, both in terms of dealing with major adversity or adjusting to change.

You could even spray a non-nuclear payload such as anthrax into the air via a small plane or radio-controlled Unmanned Aerial Vehicle (UAV) flying over a city, a technique not too dissimilar to that employed in the James Bond movie *Goldfinger*. Or you could just wait until a country such as the UK builds a national water-pipe network and pour something nasty in at one end.

So, is the idea of criminals getting hold of a stolen bomb and blackmailing a government, or corporation, pure fantasy? I'm afraid not. In 1995 rebels from Chechnya attempted to detonate a dirty bomb in Moscow, and Al-Qaeda has tried to build such devices in other countries. And it wouldn't be impossible for rogue elements from a foreign army to do something untoward without official state backing.

If and when what we fear most does happen, the main fallout will be the psychological effects, because people are not as mentally resilient or practical as they were half a century ago. This is partly due to circumstances – we have not been mentally or physically tested for at least a generation, and many of our technological 'advances' are shielding us from reality, both in its current form and in terms of what may one day exist. Many people nowadays cannot even wire a plug or fix a broken vehicle let alone kill an animal for food or deal with dead bodies. We would eventually recover from any such incident, I imagine, but in the shorter term, chaos and lunacy would almost certainly reign.

> **❝The era of nuclear terrorism has arrived.❞**
>
> **Liam Fox, former British Defence Secretary**

the condensed idea
Beware terrorists with nuclear materials

44 Volcanoes & quakes

In 1815, a volcano known as Tambora erupted on an island called Sumbawa in Indonesia. The eruption was the most powerful ever recorded. It has been linked, by some people, to what became known as 'The Year Without Summer', where unusually low temperatures and ash clouds led to crop failures, severe food shortages and riots. So are we due for another terrible summer?

We think we're clever. We believe that we're in control of our own destiny and that nature has been more or less tamed by mankind. How very deluded we all are. The problem, to a very large extent, is individual and collective memory once again. We tend to forget what happened geologically a very long time ago and focus on the geological present and very immediate future. Hence we can barely remember the San Francisco earthquake of 1989 or the Los Angeles earthquake of 1994, unless we were living in San Francisco or Los Angeles at the time. As for the event that occurred around 3,200 BC, evidence suggests that this included a flood of biblical proportions, but, despite our history books, we've forgotten about this too, unless you happen to be a fan of Noah and the Old Testament. And let's not forget about asteroids and locust plagues, although we usually do.

We continually build and expand towns and cities beside large rivers, next to vast oceans, beneath 'extinct' volcanoes and above known fault lines. Why do we do this? Probably because we are essentially optimistic, hopeful, pragmatic, forgetful or just plain silly. This can work to our

timeline

1815	1883	1906	1960
Tambora eruption	Krakatoa eruption	San Francisco earthquake	Chilean earthquake

advantage for a very long time, but evidence of recent and not-so-recent natural disasters and geological events would seem to suggest that eventually we get seriously caught out and that the consequences can be dramatic.

The next big blow Tambora was the biggest bang for 1,300 years and it's hard for non-experts, myself included, to get their heads around just how big this explosion was. Suffice to say that darkness increased, temperatures fell, Byron wrote his poem 'Darkness' and Mary Shelley sketched out the plot for Frankenstein. This was by all accounts a very big bang. Toba, in Indonesia, about 70,000–77,000 years ago, was even bigger, probably the largest explosion on Earth in the past 25 million years.

Recent eruptions have been tiddlers in comparison. But every 100,000 years or so a very large volcanic eruption takes place and one is now well overdue. In recent years the largest eruption was Pinatubo in the Philippines, but this was small, erupting about 10km³ (2.4 cubic miles) of material. Krakatoa, in 1883, erupted 19 km³ (4.6 cubic miles) and Santorini in Greece around 3,600 years ago erupted 30–33 km³ (7–7.9 cubic miles) of material. Tambora erupted 100km³ (24 cubic miles), so it was about ten times the scale of Pinatubo.

Big bang

How you view earthquakes, volcanoes and tsunamis depends on where you live. If you live in Japan, for instance, you'll be all too familiar with the destructive power of nature. If you live in San Francisco, and are relatively young, you will be less familiar. However, what we all have in common is that within living memory nobody has experienced what happens when a super-volcano explodes. Hopefully, nobody will know for at least a few thousand years. We'd cope, of course, but one sometimes wonders what the fallout would be in a world where supply-chain tolerances are so tight. The world is now interconnected like never before and global companies that source and transport components from all over the world cannot cope for long with major disturbances or disruptions in critical regions.

> **❛It is not a question of "if", it is a question of when.❜**
>
> **Bill McGuire,** Aon Benfield Hazard Research Centre, UCL, referring to a super-eruption

2010	2011	2028	2056
Icelandic Eyjafjallajökull volcano	Tokyo earthquake and tsunami	Istanbul Great Quake	Rogue asteroid strike

❝...They slept on the abyss without a surge— The waves were dead; the tides were in their grave, The Moon, their mistress, had expired before; The winds were withered in the stagnant air, And the clouds perished! Darkness had no need, Of aid from them— She was the universe❞

Lord Byron, *Darkness*, 1816

So is there a really big volcano that could blow its top any time soon? The best candidate in terms of scale and fear factor would be in Yellowstone Park in the USA. This volcano famously exploded around 1.3 million years ago and erupted an estimated 1,000km³ (240 cubic miles) of material. In contrast, in 1980, Mount St Helens in the USA erupted just 1km³ (0.24 cubic miles) of material. Yellowstone is huge, as we can see from evidence of previous eruptions, and it tends to explode every 600,000 years or so. When was the last really big Yellowstone eruption? About 600,000 years ago!

Dire results So what might happen if Yellowstone, or another super-volcano, exploded during our lifetime? Nobody knows, of course, but the implications could be truly devastating.

First, the explosion would physically remove anything even remotely nearby and the loss of tree cover could potentially result in major soil erosion, mud jams and floods.

Second, pyroclastic (superheated) flows of molten rock would wipe out anything remotely in their path and vast dust clouds would cause havoc locally and potentially globally too (remember that tiny volcano in Iceland that brought international air travel to a grinding halt in 2010? Well a super-volcano might be ten, one hundred or even a thousand times worse).

However, the biggest consequence would almost certainly be climate change. Concentrations of dust, sulphur dioxide and carbon dioxide might lead to what some people have termed a volcanic winter – or a second Year Without Summer. Temperatures could collapse rapidly, the Sun might literally disappear from view, food crops could fail and foods prices go through the roof, and people could starve, especially in remote and disadvantaged regions. This, in turn, could trigger unregulated mass-population movements or potentially the downfall of

The end of the world?

There are some weird ideas out there and those relating to December 21, 2012 are especially strange. They may, of course, be correct, in which case you probably won't be reading this, but I'm erring on the side of unbridled optimism on this point. Some people claim that the Mayan calendar says that the world will end on December 21, 2012. Why might this occur? One commentator (a website called Armageddon online) says it's to do with shifts in magnetic fields. The same commentator gives odds of 10:1 against a super-volcano erupting on the same date.

governments if they failed to respond effectively. Air transport could grind to a halt, and with it parts of the global logistics industry, companies could fail and people could lose their jobs. You might even speculate that it's possible, although not very likely, that microscopic particles of volcanic dust could find their way deep inside various machines and devices that we rely on – stopping them from working. And that's before we even consider wars linked to the food shortages.

That's not it either. That's just super-volcanoes. Other potentially devastating super-events might include a major eruption that triggers an earthquake, which triggers a series of other earthquakes or a tsunami the scale of which we've never experienced before. All of these events are highly unlikely to occur within our lifetimes, but they're not impossible and if they were to occur the impacts could be catastrophic.

the condensed idea
Geologically speaking, we've been lucky

45 The sixth mass extinction

Of all the species that have ever existed on our planet, 95 per cent are now believed to be extinct. Mass extinction events have occurred many times on Earth, but five 'big kills' over the past 540 million years or so have resulted in around 75 per cent of all animal species disappearing. Could *Homo sapiens* be next?

Not so long ago species were essentially thought of as fixed. Then Darwin came along and argued that species slowly evolved in relation to changing conditions. He was right, but he was wrong about one important element – the speed of change. It now appears that sometimes evolution can happen relatively quickly and it's now generally agreed that a sixth mass extinction event could be occurring at this very moment, with as many as half of the world's current species becoming extinct by the end of the present century. Possible culprits include habitat fragmentation, loss of biodiversity, ecosystem stresses, manmade transformation of the natural landscape (especially through agriculture), disease, pollution, the introduction of invasive alien plant (and animal) species, climate change and a range of other human activities.

Species that are threatened include a number of amphibians, especially in Europe, bats and the turtle dove – the latter is in serious trouble in the UK due to the disappearance of various plants that have been ploughed up or removed by intensive agriculture and the use of various weedkillers on and around farmland.

timeline

1662	**1966**	**1989**	**1998**
Dodo becomes extinct	Last Arabian ostrich	Golden toads extinct	Poll of 400 scientists reveals that 70 per cent believe mass extinction is happening

A sting in the tale Bees could also be in serious trouble, although the reasons for this remain far from clear. What we do know is that bees are currently essential for pollinating many of the world's food crops, with as much as 33 per cent of everything we eat being dependent upon natural pollination by bees, hoverflies or moths. On the other hand, this could be yet another case of scaremongering. Critics argue that bee loss is partly a US phenomena, with bee numbers increasing by around 45 per cent globally. Second, while bees are indeed vital for pollination, many of our food staples such as wheat, rice and corn depend on wind pollination. But what if the pessimists are right?

Techno-optimists might say that it could one day be possible to replace natural bees with tiny robotic pollinating UAV 'insects', but that,

> **Once you lose species, you don't get them back. It takes millions of years to rebound from a mass extinction event.**
>
> Nicholas Matzke,
> **University of California at Berkeley**

Previous mass extinctions

The first major mass extinction occurred around 440 million years ago and appears related to sudden global cooling ('sudden' being a relative term geologically speaking). The second major mass extinction, 370 million years ago, may also have been related to climate change. For the third and fourth mass extinctions, causes are a little more elusive, but it could have been climate change mixed with tectonic movements. As for the fifth mass extinction, which happened around 65 million years ago and involved the dinosaurs, many experts believe that this was either caused by the impact of one or more asteroids or one or more super-volcanoes (see Chapter 44).

2000	2005	2006	2035
Last Pyrenean Ibex dies (it's cloned back in 2009 but later dies)	Extinct Laotian Rock Rat rediscovered	Freshwater dolphin declared dead	50 per cent of European amphibians extinct

presumably, is of very little consolation to the bees or for hungry human beings over the shorter term. As for some of the other threatened species, you could argue that we don't really need elephants or giant pandas nowadays. They will soon be gone and we'll just have to get over it. But this argument misses a very critical point – in a great many cases there is a delicate relationship between one species and another; if you remove one species, this can eventually lead to the collapse or at least the radical rearrangement of another, or in extreme cases the removal of entire ecosystems.

In other words, the natural world is a highly complex and massively interrelated system in which one species tends to have a symbiotic relationship with other species, although sometimes this is not immediately obvious. We've talked about the implications of ubiquitous connectivity from a technological perspective elsewhere in this book, but this connectively applies to the natural world too.

Out interconnected world The last flapping of a butterfly's wings deep in a remote forest can have a catastrophic effect on other species, including complacent animals at the top of the evolutionary tree. Will we and other species adapt to our new and rapidly changing

Smart or just lucky?

Studying subjects such as history, physics or biology helps us grasp just how insignificant our current concerns are. We are, as it were, just passing through. As a people, and as a planet, we are destined to become nothing but stardust. Of course, there are two obvious ways of dealing with this thought. One is essentially fatalistic. Whatever we do is unimportant in the grand scheme of things, so let's not worry about anything, including climate change or nuclear proliferation. The other option is more optimistic and more proactive. As a species we have survived thus far and, if we really are alone in the universe, it should be our duty to preserve what we have and extend ourselves as far as we can for as long as we can.

environment or will a series of unfortunate events combine to create a sixth and final (for us at least) extinction event in the future? Obviously nobody knows, but a number of experts are quite concerned and if extreme climate change is also factored in, things start to look very worrying indeed. Will species adapt? Will they physically move or will they die out altogether and over what timescale? Probably the most difficult question of all to answer is how all of the various changes will combine. As to how many species may die out, this is also unclear, but it could be at least one thousand times the natural rate.

> **If you look only at the critically endangered mammals … that puts us clearly outside any range of normal, and tells us that we are moving into the mass extinction realm.**
>
> Anthony D. Barnosky,
> **Professor of Integrative Biology**

The doomsday scenario is clearly that we are about to die out and be replaced with another dominant species. This may or may not happen. Some people, such as James Lovelock, have argued that by the end of this century just a handful of breeding pairs of human beings will be left, probably in the Arctic where weather conditions will remain tolerable.

Of course, there's also the argument that instead of adapting to the changing environment, human beings will adapt the environment to our changing requirements (see Chapter 10). This argument is quite plausible over the much longer term. However, smart as we are, especially over extended time periods, we can be remarkably stupid, blinkered and stubborn over much shorter time periods and for this reason the clock could be ticking on humankind's time on Earth.

There's also the point that human beings have no God-given right (in my view) to inherit, or manage, the Earth. Other species were here before us and they may well remain long after we've gone. In other words, the Earth itself is not under threat. The Earth is highly resilient and will adapt over geological time.

the condensed idea
Are we on the way out?

46 The Singularity

Moore's Law (named after Gordon Moore) says that computers double their processing ability every 18 months or so. But imagine if this rate of exponential growth was itself exponential. That's one potential consequence of what future tech-heads call the 'Singularity', where computers will be able to create AGIs (artificial general intelligences) more intelligent than human beings.

Proponents of the Singularity, most notably the inventor and futurist Ray Kurzweil, say that if computers continue to advance at their current rate, the singularity is a mere 20–30 years away – perhaps sooner if useful quantum computers are developed. Intel is already reinventing the humble transistor by harnessing photons and quantum properties to increase processing power, and Kurzweil has set up the so-called Singularity University, backed by Google and NASA, to educate the next generation in making the Singularity possible. Even the British scientist Stephen Hawking believes it's possible.

Whether it happens suddenly, or over time, it appears that machines will become increasingly sophisticated and able to do much of the work of human beings. One commentator says: 'As our machines become more like us, we will become more like them.' Perhaps machines will get smarter and more mobile while the human population becomes less intelligent and ever-more housebound as a direct result.

Any true AGI would need at least four capabilities to be like us: to recognize objects, handle complex dialogue, be manually dextrous, and understand social situations from someone else's point of view. Children

timeline

2011	2040	2045	2050
Voice declines significantly as a human-to-human communication medium	AGI (artificial general intelligence) exists	The distinction between virtual and real life becomes almost meaningless	Full virtual-reality immersion

If it can be done, can we resist doing it?

There are two ways of thinking about the Singularity. One is that it's inevitable. Our brains are only atoms and we will one day work out precisely how they work, then replicate them artificially. It's a question of *when?* and *how?* rather than *if* or *thou shalt not*. The second approach is that it's more or less impossible and we really shouldn't even try, because if we accidentally succeed we would be forced to upturn some of our strongest beliefs and confront some of our deepest fears. But perhaps that's just human anxiety. Maybe in the future we will just accept the fact that the technology exists, make the best of it and ask philosophers to redefine what being human really means.

start to learn each of these skills slowly until the age of eight, when all are present. There is no reason why robots could not be made to deal with whatever tasks they're required to do, whether it's putting groceries away or babysitting. But will they be able to fall in love or truly empathize with a person in physical pain or suffering from mental anguish?

I doubt it. Many of our emotions have their origins in biological imperatives encoded into our genes thousands of years ago. To make machines behave in a similar manner would require them to be preloaded with equally irrational behaviours.

Economic drive Some say that the agricultural and industrial revolutions were singularities, because of the rapid pace of change compared to what had gone before. Over the past 7,000 years, output doubled every 900 years. Now output

> **❝What if not everyone wants to go along with this?❞**
>
> Ray Kurzweil, author, inventor and futurist

2060	2070	2080	2095
The first human brain enters a machine body	Computer viruses become the main threat to human existence	Scientists acknowledge that immortality exists for those that want it	Human-robot hybrids (brains in boxes) take off to explore distant galaxies

doubles roughly every 15 years, about 60 times as fast as in the previous seven millennia. The next radical jump will come from shortages in our economy: first resources and energy and then, perhaps, human time and attention. If robots were able to take over most of what people currently do (and two-thirds of a nation's income is paid directly in wages), there would be a massive jump in output, freeing human beings for other more satisfying forms of work.

Or perhaps not. After all, every time a new labour-saving device is invented we seem to end up with less free time not more. Why? Possibly because we up our expectations of what we expect ourselves or others to do or produce. There's also the thought that rising automation will lead to mass unemployment and a Luddite revolution.

It's cheaper to build robots than it is to pay someone over a lifetime. Robots don't need to sleep or take holidays either. But the value of human work could still rise, especially if some of us prefer to be served by human beings and are willing to pay extra for it. Again, we can get a glimpse of this already: if you shop at a supermarket, you often have the option to be 'served' by a machine rather than a real person. Automated scanning and checkouts seem to suit some people and not others. Similar 'robots without heads, arms and legs' can be found in post offices and airline check-in desks. We are already surrounded by these robots, so an interesting question to ponder is not whether they will multiply (they will) but what we will do with their highly intelligent (and technically impartial) cousins? Will they replace law-enforcement officials, teachers, judges and so on?

> **❝I have argued that we cannot prevent the Singularity, that its coming is an inevitable consequence of the humans' natural competitiveness and the possibilities inherent in technology.❞**
>
> **Vernor Vinge, computer scientist, professor of mathematics and sci-fi author**

The human dimension Robots that do solely cognitive work may live in virtual environments and be essentially invisible, while others will exist in human environments and be more lifelike. Kurzweil sees something more radical: a 'merger of biological and non-biological intelligence' culminating in 'immortal software-based humans'. But at what point could a machine be declared human, and if a machine were to be so declared, would it be deserving of human-like rights?

Digital immortality

It may sound like science fiction, but the story of computing has been thus all along. A high-profile figure in the Singularity world is Raymond Kurzweil – a maverick or a genius depending on your point of view. He says Moore's Law is just the beginning. The combination of increasing computing power and the creation of cyborg humans will lead to an unprecedented opportunity to 'address humanity's grand challenges'. He claims it will even be possible one day to upload the contents of our brains to a computer, thus creating a kind of immortality where man (and it would probably be a man!) merges with machine.

It's a frightening thought for some that computers could one day become more intelligent than we are. But it also assumes that it's possible to know the depths of the human mind and then produce something better. Is it really conceivable to analyse every dendrite, axon and synapse of the human brain and be able to re-create it? Is this a naively reductionist approach to human life that serves us well for building computers but is profoundly lacking when it comes to creating human life? Moreover, an intellect would not need to be human-like to be reckoned with. In many ways it could be worse to deal with if it were not, because it's entirely possible that such an intellect could not be reasoned with using human logic or emotion.

the condensed idea
Machines much
smarter than people

47 Me or we?

One of the driving forces of change over the past 50 years or so has been the rise of the individual. Recently, technology and legislation have both amplified and accelerated individualism. But could things one day move in another direction? Could connectivity, along with climate change and resource shortages, shift our focus back to the primacy of the group or society at large?

We live in a world that is increasingly global, urban, restless and rootless. We're told that we're all unique and that within certain limits we're all free to do anything, believe anything or be anything, regardless of the wider impacts these actions or beliefs may have. Not all nations are like this, of course, but it's largely assumed that one day they more or less all will be.

There are already plenty of arguments about the direction that capitalism should take in the future, and some people are questioning whether democracy and the pursuit of individual happiness are creating bigger problems than they're solving. Nevertheless, in the vast majority of nations the focus is still very much on the individual and we are witnessing a global outbreak of Me-ism, where unrestrained capitalism, together with a sense of entitlement and individual rights, trump any thought of humility, restraint, deference or personal responsibility. Furthermore, technology is acting as an accelerant to this trend globally. Products and experiences that were once largely rationed, or communally accessed, are increasingly becoming available to individuals. Digitalization, for example, means that many products and experiences can now be personalized to suit the whims and wishes of individual users.

timeline

1776	1848	1859	1962
Wealth of Nations published	*Communist Manifesto* published	*On Liberty* published	*Silent Spring* published

Your problem is mine

Open innovation, an idea originally pioneered by the open-source software community, has the potential to radically change how and where our problems are solved. In one sense the wisdom of crowds is no different from old-fashioned suggestion boxes, but the big difference is scale and to some extent speed. With enough networked minds, all problems become shallow. Linked to this idea is another, namely collaborative consumption. This is the use of connecting technologies to allow people to share and exchange all kinds of physical and digital goods, services, assets and skills.

Media is an example. Once it was narrowly broadcast and tightly controlled by a few for the many. There wasn't much democracy, but it was a communal experience. Now media is increasingly created and consumed by individuals and its fragmentary and atomized nature means that you can find whatever interests you personally and have it delivered on a device of your choosing at any time, any place, anywhere. Web 2.0 builds upon this impulse. It's YOUtube and MYspace and everyone is famous for 15 minutes and to 15 people. At its worst, this is postmodernism

❝For good or ill, we live in an interdependent world. We can't escape each other. Therefore, we have to spend our lives building a global community of shared responsibilities, shared values, shared benefits.❞

Bill Clinton, former President of the United States

1972	2017	2023	2029
The Limits to Growth published	*Common Sense Manifesto* published	*Nordic Capitalism* published	*The Chinese Way* published

Digital Maoism?

Jaron Lanier, sometimes referred to as the creator of the term 'virtual reality', believes that crowd intelligence is something of a fallacy analogous with the belief of hyper-libertarians that the free market is all-wise and ultimately benefits all. To quote Lanier: 'The beauty of the Internet is that it connects people. The value is in the other people. If we start to believe that the Internet itself is an entity that has something to say, we're devaluing those people and making ourselves into idiots.' The danger with crowd-sourced wisdom is that the aggregator may become more important and influential than the aggregated. Taken to the extreme, collective intelligence would mean that individuals would not be required to make individual judgements or take on individual responsibilities.

and subjectivism gone mad. It's a world where idiocy, shallowness and superficiality reign supreme, because everyone's life, skill or opinion is as good as everyone else's.

Coming together? But how long will this last? Presently, our newfound hyper-connectivity is making many of us lonely. We have begun to trade intimacy for familiarity and we no longer connect deeply with anything or anyone any more. Maybe this won't change. Perhaps things will be even more personalized in the future and short-term hedonism and indulgence will flourish at the expense of empathy and sustainability. We'll all be living a life that's highly sensory, interactive and individual. Our own iPad oblivion.

This situation may endure. Or there may be another, more plausible, scenario – that resource shortages, together with climate change and digital connectivity, will bring people together physically and mentally.

We will become alarmed about the health of our planet and especially the pervasive influence of materialism and consumerism upon our lives and will decide to do something about it – collectively. This isn't exactly the end of free markets and globalization, but both would be restrained for the sake of the common good over the longer term. In this future world, altruism takes over from selfishness and people rediscover the joys of simplicity, slowness and balance. It's more local too. Crucially, we also rediscover and reconnect with the idea that it's only through direct connection with other individuals that our lives have any real meaning.

Addressing the issues In 2011, Sherry Turkle, a professor of Social Studies of Science and Technology at MIT, published a book called *Alone Together: Why We Expect More from Technology and Less from Each Other*. In it she argued that while new technologies allow us to do anything, anywhere, they're draining and depleting us, especially when physical human interaction is removed from our everyday lives. As she puts it: 'We seem determined to give human qualities to objects and content to treat each other as things.' So perhaps another future is an uncomfortable mixture of two quite separate ideals. Globally we'll be connected as one. We'll have access to anything or anyone we want. But locally it will be a different story. We become increasingly isolated and use technology to displace our true feelings.

How we address the question of whether it's the individual or the wider community that's more important is a critical question going forward. It impacts on everything from the delivery of education, health, transport, pensions and even policing – things that were once publicly provided, but are increasingly becoming privatized. It's a question that needs to be urgently considered by both individuals and society alike.

> **More and more, when faced with the world of men, the only reaction is one of individualism. Man alone is an end unto himself. Everything one tries to do for the common good ends in failure.**
>
> **Albert Camus, novelist and essayist**

the condensed idea
Just one versus everyone

48 Mind modification

Everything we experience throughout our lives changes our brains, so why wouldn't something we've started doing rather a lot of recently change our minds fundamentally in the future? Modern technology, in particular the Internet and mobile computing, may be doing just this and the results could affect not only how we see ourselves, but how we react to each other.

The average American adult spends five hours a day on a computer, tablet device or smartphone. But if it's like this now imagine what it could be like when communication gets even faster thanks to predictive technologies, voice-to-machine interfaces and implanted communication devices. This is an accelerated, metallic, automated and extrovert future full of digital interruptions. A world of sensory overload totally lacking in the kind of stillness and quiet necessary to understand not only ideas, but ourselves.

No doubt we'll get better at quickly filtering and processing information. Our thinking will become fast, fluid and flexible, but what would be lost as a result? It could be that the cost we'll pay for such easy connectivity and communication will include a loss of rigorous, focused and reflective thinking. We may also see a loss of deep human connection, empathy and understanding. One US study, by Sara Konrath, has found a 40 per cent drop in empathy among college students over the past 20 or 30 years.

In the future perhaps we'll become more lost in personalized and hedonistic bubbles of information and entertainment, cut off from the

timeline

2011	2012	2020	2035
Average adult spends five hours a day on a screen	Overall IQ scores drop for the first time in a decade	Average attention span now less than two minutes	Kids spend more time in virtual worlds than in real life

real world and its problems by high-definition screens and headphones. We'll understand things intellectually, but we'll struggle to comprehend the same things emotionally.

What this means for our brains Another downside could be a loss of originality, either because we'll feel pressured to fall into line with the majority of online opinion (easily visible, along with your own point of view, to the rest of the world) or because we'll simply do whatever is most convenient – such as looking only at the first page of Google search results (which 99 per cent of us do already). A loss of privacy may also encourage conservatism. If future technology favours remembering over forgetting, perhaps individuals will experiment less or be less willing to make the mistakes that true originality requires.

> **We shape our tools and thereafter our tools shape us.**
>
> **Marshall McLuhan, Canadian educator and philosopher**

Why are screens so addictive?

Why is it becoming so difficult to get children to play outside rather than staying inside using computer games? There are various explanations, not least that they're fun, entertaining and provide a sense of achievement. They are also convenient, especially for time-pressed and exhausted parents. The problem here is that what's increasingly normal is structured or rule-based play. According to a 2005 study published in the *Archives of Paediatrics & Adolescent Medicine*, incidences of free play declined by 25 per cent between 1981 and 1997 and this may be resulting in children who are socially inept and have difficulty dealing with stress and anxiety. It may also mean less creativity and original thinking, especially in later life.

2038	**2040**	**2055**	**2060**
Adults talking to personal avatars more than partners	iPads widely withdrawn from schools following steep drop in IQ scores	Unauthorized expropriation of human attention becomes a crime	Slow-thinking movement leads to drift away from screens

But how is all this possible from a neurological standpoint? The answer is simple. Our brains are 'plastic' in the sense that they physically respond to whatever they're exposed to. This is true throughout our lives, but it's especially true with young children. So our minds are just as vulnerable as the rest of our bodies when it comes to what we do with them. This isn't just a case of 'garbage in, garbage out', but of mind modification and even atrophy. It's a bit like forgetting how to do mental arithmetic if you always use a calculator. Your brain is like a muscle and you have to keep exercising it.

How will a mind that's been immersed in connectivity, interactivity, personalization, virtual sensation and instant reward from birth think in the future? How will we think when we're never truly alone because we're constantly connected, either to each other or to an endless stream of rapid-fire information? How will we think when we first need to see what everyone else thinks? Perhaps what will happen is that reading and writing will die out, replaced by watching. Maybe this, in turn, will be replaced with direct brain-to-machine interfaces, our thoughts being used not only to control objects and actions, but also to communicate with each other via neurotelepathy.

Flexible thinking Who can really say what will happen, but perhaps such a mind won't think, or at least it won't think in the same way that we're used to thinking now, because thinking, as we have historically thought of it, will become less relevant. If this all sounds like human nature being fluid rather than fixed that's true. Human nature is usually thought of as static, but that's because our external environment has been more or less fixed historically too. If we're fundamentally changing the world in which we live, perhaps our nature, especially our emotional needs, will change.

> **If you buy into the idea that the mind is the personalization of the brain, the organization of neuronal connections through experience, then that brain will be highly vulnerable to 21st-century technology.**
>
> Susan Greenfield,
> Senior Research Fellow, University Department of Pharmacology, Oxford University

This could be a good thing. Perhaps global connectivity will open up our minds to what others think and we will see the world for what it really is – a fragile planet facing serious problems. If this is the case, the hope is that we'll reap the rewards of the creativity and generosity promised by the Internet age.

Wise up

According to Steven Johnson, author of *Everything Bad is Good for You*, popular culture (everything from old episodes of *Law & Order* to computer games from *Angry Birds* to *Call of Duty* and *Grand Theft Auto*) is far more intellectually demanding than it used to be and individuals are being forced, whether they like it or not, to work a little bit harder mentally to participate. In other words, our external environment is indeed changing, but this is having a hugely positive effect in terms of our abstract reasoning skills. So screen culture is actually making us smarter.

Or perhaps events will take a more sinister turn. Maybe we'll become lazy and stop reading serious books (too long, too difficult) and focus instead on a world of shallow celebrity and opinion. We'll immerse ourselves in novelty and fantasy and become reckless in our dealings with the real world. Perhaps we'll retreat into virtual realities, although, of course, its possible that in the future the word 'real' will have no actual meaning once we implant devices into our own bodies and augment reality with personalized overlays of digital information. We might also see radical cosmetic surgery becoming more mainstream, and this might encourage individuals to experiment with different physical personalities as they already do online. How all of this will change us is anyone's guess, although it seems reasonable to assume that our sense of self would change along with our behaviour.

the condensed idea
Will we still be ourselves?

49 Is God back?

It's often been assumed that the future will be a godless place. That economic development, along with science and the spread of democracy, will create a secularist world where religion will be on its knees. Institutional Christianity is indeed in trouble, but other traditional religions such as Islam are booming. So what's next – a resurgent Christianity, militant atheism or religious wars?

The argument that God is dead, found most famously in the works of the German philosopher Friedrich Nietzsche, is credible, but the message is mixed. In some regions, organized belief is being superseded by secularism, militant atheism, celebrity fervour and a belief in science over other forms of wonder. With Christianity in Europe, for example, things are looking bleak. One conceivable outcome is marginalization alongside Islam or against a plethora of new sects, celebrity cults and personal religions where populist preachers offer instant gratification in the 'church of me right now'. The reaction of Christian Churches to this will, in all probability, be to update themselves to ensure their relevance in today's world, but in so doing they risk distancing themselves from the one thing that would ensure their survival – a clear path to the next world. It is, of course, true that in many parts of Africa and Asia, formal Christian worship is expanding. Worship is resilient in the USA too, but radical sects and shallow evangelism underpin much of this growth, as do radical sects in many developing regions, and this is unlikely to last for long.

Changing belief systems Doing well right now, globally, is religious fervour minus the religion. Celebrities generate worship-like hysteria across the world, while successful businesses tap into the messianic

timeline

1883	1966	2005	2009
Friedrich Nietzsche claims that God is dead	*Time* magazine asks 'Is God dead?'	Sermons via text message	Virtual funeral ceremonies

delusions of their followers. It's websites not worship, and iPads not the Book of Job. But, again, how long will this last? Putting on a pair of far-sighted glasses, things start to look very different.

First there's the idea that in a world of crumbling confidence and unending uncertainty, traditional religions can continue to do what they've always done: they explain the unexplainable and provide meaning in a world full of chaos. Secularism, in contrast, is quite literally meaningless. As for science destroying religion, the very opposite could end up being true. We may find that the more we find out about the universe, the less we understand it and the more confused we become, which could benefit religion with its simple rules and explanations.

There's also the thought that as science delves further into the origins of our universe we may find out that ours is not the only one (see Chapter 40). There may be other parallel universes (multiverses), which might help to

> **❝Religions come and go but mostly they come and stay.❞**
>
> **Felipe Fernández-Armesto,**
> **historian and author**

growth markets for god

In 1900, 80 per cent of Christians lived in Europe or the USA. Nowadays, 60 per cent live in the developing world. In China, for example, there are 80 million active Christians, which means that the Christian Church is bigger than the Communist Party in membership terms. By 2050 it's predicted that there could be almost 220 million Christians in China, or around 16 per cent of its total population, while in Russia, 86 per cent of people classify themselves as Christian. So while traditional belief is declining rapidly, or stagnating in some regions, it's expanding rapidly in many others, especially in those regions forecast to have most robust population growth in the future.

2011	2020	2030	2050
US study predicts religion may become extinct in nine countries	Catholic Church under pressure to support euthanasia	First female pope	Return of the Messiah (but this time she's called Kylie)

> **Perhaps our role on this planet is not to worship God – but to create Him.**
>
> Arthur C. Clarke,
> sci-fi author, inventor and futurist

explain the notion of heaven and hell. Equally, we may find a way of communicating via thought alone (neurotelepathy), an idea that links to the use of prayer to communicate with unseen gods. Or how about the separation of body and soul? This currently sounds ridiculous to some, but if one day we understand what consciousness is, perhaps we'll be able to isolate it and put it somewhere else, thereby creating creatures of pure consciousness – spirits by another name.

Demographics are another reason for supporters of traditional religion to be optimistic. High fertility rates underpin much of the growth of Islam, while increased longevity means larger numbers of older people – who are interested in deep questions about what comes next. There's the argument that the aim of living longer may itself become a religion (see Chapter 35), but we'll have to deal with that if and when it happens.

Another trend feeding traditional religion is urbanization. Hundreds of millions of people are moving into urban areas, and this makes for atomized, rootless and restless societies. Religion, once again, offers people a community and identity that is secure.

Admittedly, the wealth that often flows from urbanization can be an enemy of traditional religion. Why? Because money can buy immediate comfort and a life of superficial distraction and sensory pleasure, all of which block deep thought and reflection. However, as we've already seen, a quest for happiness is starting to shine a light on whether or not material goods produce long-term satisfaction.

Finally, there's technology. We'll explore one of the impacts of rapid technological change next, but suffice to say that anxiety created by complexity and the speed of change is likely to play out well for religions that emphasize permanence, simplicity, history and tradition.

Fulfilling a need Is there anything else that mainstream religions should fear over the longer-term? Various cults and sects will appeal to the anxieties of our age, but their intellectual underpinnings will be too shallow for them to keep standing firm for long. There is also paganism. Strangely, this may do well due to our desire for magic in a scientific

The god Particle

Could something that many people strongly believe in, but nobody has ever seen, change how we think about life on Earth? The Higgs boson is a subatomic particle that scientists predicted would one day be discovered. It just has, and may soon go some way to explaining why things exist in the way that they do. It certainly explains where mass comes from, which should, in turn, explain why things exist the way they do in the universe. The question, of course, is whether this new discovery will help to destroy the idea of creationism or merely uncover further questions about how and why the universe was created.

age. What we might end up with, therefore, is science living alongside superstition. This leaves the more established religions, whose greatest worry may be each other. Historically, when religions feel secure their followers have a tendency to fight each other and I see no reason why this impulse will go away.

So there we have it. Mainstream or traditional religions will survive because we will need them. The future will be confusing and religions will provide explanation. They will provide rules on how to behave, as well as something else that human beings, uniquely, appear to need – meaning. Somehow, most of us just can't live (or die) with the thought that there's nothing else out there. What people need most is the promise of a future, and what the future needs most is the reassurance and continuity of the distant past.

the condensed idea
God is not dead

50 Future shock

It's the end of the world. At least that's how many people are feeling. We're still reeling from 9/11, the global financial crisis, climate change and political upheaval. It feels as though change has itself changed and we're all struggling to keep up. But will this last? Perhaps the issue is that we're currently exposing ourselves to too much information and this is resulting in temporary disorientation.

In the early 1970s, Alvin Toffler wrote a best-selling book called *Future Shock*. The author argued that too much technological change, or at least the perception of too much rapid change, over what was felt to be too short a period of time, was resulting in psychological damage to individuals and even to society as a whole. Toffler also placed the term 'information overload' into the general consciousness.

In many ways, the concept of future shock is similar to that of culture shock. Both refer to the way in which individuals feel disorientated when they quickly move from one familiar way of life to another. In the case of culture shock, this usually refers to physical movement from one country, or culture, to another. In the case of future shock, we might use the term to describe the shift from analogue to digital culture or from a period containing what were thought of as fixed truths and geopolitical certainties to an era where boundaries are fluid and nothing feels certain. The danger here, of course, is that such anxiety and bewilderment is fertile ground for false prophets of order and populist politicians who promise final solutions.

The rapid-change argument is certainty plausible. Adherents to this argument could cite Moore's Law (see Chapter 17), the rapid rate of

timeline

1400s	1800s	1839
'Printed books will never be the equivalent of handwritten codices.' Trithemius, *De Laude Scriptorum*	'Rail travel at high speed is not possible because passengers, unable to breathe, would die of asphyxia.' Dr Dionysys Lardner	'The abolishment of pain in surgery is a chimera. It is absurd to go on seeking it ... ' Dr Alfred Velpeau, surgeon

development in genetics, robotics, artificial intelligence and nanotechnology or the breathless expansion of social media. By the time you read this, it might be necessary to add further upheavals in the Middle East, Europe or developments in China. But was it not ever thus? The Internet, a fundamentally disruptive development, can be compared in terms of impact to the rapid development of the telegraph, the railways or electricity in Victorian times. As for the Middle East, Europe or China, history tends to repeat itself, often as tragedy and sometimes as farce, as Karl Marx observed. So why are we feeling so ill at ease? Why is doom and gloom in the ascendant? Why are we so worried all of a sudden? Will our current anxieties slowly evaporate or will they suddenly shift from bad to worse?

> **The only thing we know about the future, is that it will be different.**
>
> **Peter Drucker,**
> **management theoretician and writer**

Do we know too much? The answer is that while events continue to go on more or less as they've always done, globalization, digitalization and above all personal connectivity mean that the reporting and distribution of such events has exploded. We have entered a period where everything is visible and to some extent knowable. Blissful ignorance is dead or, at the very least, on temporary life support.

Stressed? Don't be

In a recent poll by the American psychological society, 22 per cent of people claimed to be 'very stressed'. Seems reasonable, except that a year earlier the figure was 24 per cent. Back in 2007 it was 32 per cent. On the surface, this makes little sense, but one explanation offered by psychologists is that after five years of turmoil people might be getting used to things. Perhaps this is a temporary state and we'll just invent new fears to take our minds off things closer to home.

1888
'We are probably nearing the limit of all we can know about astronomy.'
Simon Newcomb, astronomer

1904
'Airplanes are interesting toys but of no military value.'
Marechal Ferdinand Foch

1909
'The automobile has practically reached the limit of its development'
Scientific American

> **Never let the future disturb you. You will meet it, if you have to, with the same weapons of reason which today arm you against the present.**
>
> Marcus Aurelius (AD 121–180)

Something else that doesn't help: 24-hour news cycles. There are also more actors on the stage in terms of media pundits, politicians and instant experts, all of whom thrive on the creation of short-term anxiety and crisis to which they themselves are the only answer. The reaction of some people to this new state of affairs is to switch off. The Luddites are back, only this time they're switching off iPhones rather than smashing machines. But this is a pre-technological solution to a post-industrial problem. A more practical and sustainable solution is information filtering and partial withdrawal. Over time we will learn to adjust. We'll use technologies not yet invented to filter out things that we don't need to know.

We will also get better at ignoring certain types, or sources, of information and will learn that constant connectivity isn't healthy. We will slowly rediscover the joys of temporary disconnection and start to switch off various devices at night or at weekends. We will also rediscover real sleep, which is absolutely vital to the proper processing of the daily deluge of data.

We do it to ourselves One connected point: perhaps we worry about imagined threats, or we blow real, but unlikely, risks out of all proportion because there are not enough real threats present, or maybe we somehow feel that we have only ourselves to blame. Hence the fashion for misanthropic loathing of human achievement. As the *Economist* magazine has pointed out: 'In the rich world the idea of progress has become impoverished. The popular view is that, although technology and GDP advance, morals and society are treading water or, depending on your choice of newspaper, sinking back into decadence and barbarism.'

According to Dr Richard Landes, an apocalypse expert at Boston University in the USA, our enthusiasm for apocalypse is also connected with our own sense of our own importance: 'It appeals to our megalomania,' he says.

1923	1948	1956	1968
'There is no likelihood man can ever tap the power of the atom.' Robert Millikan, Nobel Prize in Physics	'Television won't last. It's a flash in the pan.' Mary Somerville, pioneer of radio educational broadcasts	'Space travel is utter bilge.' Richard van der Riet Woolley, Astronomer Royal	'But what ... is it good for?' Engineer at the Advanced Computing Systems Division of IBM (commenting on the microchip)

Future Hype

In his book *Future Hype* Bob Seidensticker points out that the current rate of change is not notably faster than in previous periods and that in many instances the so-called 'revolutionary' technologies are in fact only refinements of much earlier breakthroughs. The Internet, for example, has indeed developed quickly. But the telegraph moved from being a demonstration in 1844 to being ubiquitous in most cities globally by 1860. As the scientist and Senior Vice President of research and development at HP Joel Birnbaum and the sci-fi writer Douglas Adams have both observed, technology appears abnormal, or problematic, only to those born before it becomes pervasive.

Personally, I think we should learn to relax. The fact is that some of the issues we worry about (e.g. volcanoes) do not have human causes and may not have human solutions. We will have to adapt, that's all. Having said this, we should remain vigilant. We should keep our eyes open for individuals who promise quick fixes or suggest easy targets. But over the longer term we should congratulate ourselves. Things have been far worse historically and for the majority of humankind things have never been so good. As for the future, we'll deal with it when it happens.

the condensed idea
Everything turns out OK

1979
'People won't want to play these electronic games for more than a week, not once we start selling pinball machines for the home.'
Gus Bally, Arcade Inc.

1994
'I will believe in the 500-channel world only when I see it.'
Sumner Redstone, chairman, Viacom and CBS

2002
'There is no doubt that Saddam Hussein has weapons of mass destruction.'
Dick Cheney

Glossary

3D printer A way to produce 3D objects from digital instructions and layered materials dispersed or sprayed on via a printer.

Affective computing Machines and systems that recognize or simulate human effects or emotions.

AGI Artificial general intelligence, a term usually used to describe strong AI (the opposite of narrow or weak AI). It is machine intelligence that is equivalent to, or exceeds, human intelligence and it's usually regarded as the long-term goal of AI research and development.

Ambient intelligence Electronic or artificial environments that recognize the presence of other machines or people and respond to their needs.

Artificial photosynthesis The artificial replication of natural photosynthesis to create or store solar fuels.

Augmented reality (AR) The overlaying of digital data or information on real-world environments via mobile devices or screens. Links with modified or mediated reality and virtual reality.

Avatar assistant A customized and semi-intelligent digital assistant accessed via a mobile device or other screen.

Big data Huge data sets and vast volumes of information created by the rapidly expanding use of sensing networks and devices ranging from computers and mobile phones to GPS, RFIDs, sensor motes and smart dust. Links with data analytics and algorithms.

Bio-hacking Generally refers to the DIY manipulation, mixing and matching of genes to create different species or life-forms with novel characteristics. It can also refer to humans experimenting on or enhancing themselves or modifying other human beings.

Biomarkers An indicator of a biological state.

Biometrics The identification of individual human beings via unique characteristics or traits such as DNA, voice, fingerprints, eyes or behaviour patterns. May one day be linked to unique personal identification numbers (PINs) or passwords.

Carbon capture and sequestration Technologies and techniques that attempt to prevent the release or leakage of CO_2 into the atmosphere from the use of fossil fuels.

Claytronics The merging of computing and nanoscale robotics (and possibly artificial intelligence) to create shape-shifting materials or 3D programmable matter.

Cloud computing The remote hosting, or storage, of data, which is usually accessed on an on-demand basis. In other words, letting someone else, somewhere else, store your data, which can then be accessed any time, anywhere on any device, via the Internet.

Cloud whitening Techniques and technologies intended to modify clouds to reduce the impact of global warming. Sometimes referred to as cloud reflectivity enhancement or modification.

Context-aware computing Computers or other machines that are aware of where they are, what is around them, who a user is or what a user wants. Links with ubiquitous computing and pervasive computing, where computers are essentially in everything and everywhere.

Data mining Digging into vast mountains of information (data) to unearth useful patterns or knowledge or to predict the future behaviour of groups or individuals.

Embedded currency Digital money embedded into other objects such as mobile phones or clothing.

Energy dashboard A screen that monitors energy use in real time and may be used to monitor the performance, or cost, of individual buildings, machines, devices or appliances.

Haptic technology The use of human touch or sensation to control machines or devices or the use of artificially created tactile sensations via joysticks, gloves or clothing to give the impression that something exists or is happening when it's not. Links with gesture-based computing, virtual reality and immersive gaming.

Holographic telepresence Full-motion 3D video-conferencing or other projections of fully realistic physical presence for business or entertainment purposes.

Hydrogen economy The widescale generation and adoption of hydrogen as an alternative source of energy, especially for motive power.

Inductive charging Wireless recharging. Links to the broadcasting of electricity.

In-vitro meat Meat that is grown or cultured in a laboratory or factory without the need for a living animal.

Molecular assembly or manufacturing The human movement, or assembly, of individual molecules to produce anything you want. Links to programmable matter, claytronics and science fiction.

Nanowires Extremely small wires of unlimited length that might be used to manufacture very small machines or form part of very large structures. Links with carbon nanotubes.

Nano-generators Very small energy-harvesting devices. Could be used to generate electricity from kinetic energy (inside a pair of shoes, for example) or possibly to create artificial plants to harvest solar energy (e.g. artificial nano-grass).

Nanomedicine The medical use of nanomaterials and nano-devices. For example, medical nanobots.

Ocean fertilization A geo-engineering concept to artificially create plankton blooms in the ocean via the introduction of iron or nutrients to remove carbon dioxide from the Earth's atmosphere.

Organic human A human being who is 100 per cent natural and not genetically engineered or machine-enhanced.

Organ printing The printing of human body parts using 3D printers.

Links to the growing or 'farming' of human body parts in laboratories or factories.

Photovoltaics The generation of electrical power from solar radiation.

PMU Personal manufacturing unit - see 3D printer.

Programmable matter See Claytronics and Molecular assembly or manufacturing.

RFID Radio Frequency Identification (Device). The transfer of data (or instructions) wirelessly.

RL Real Life. See also VR.

Predictive technology Machines or devices that attempt to predict what a user will do or will want based on various inputs ranging from geographic location, time of day, interaction with other devices, search history, voice commands (speech) or text generation. Predictive texting and automated spellchecking are early examples.

Rare earths A series of rare elements or metals increasingly used in high-technology machinery and devices.

Smart agents Generally, software that exhibits a level of intelligence or understanding.

Smart dust Very small sensors that are networked wirelessly.

Swarm robotics Robots that swarm together or display crowd-like behaviour. Links with swarm intelligence, collective intelligence, hive minds and so on.

Telemedicine Medicine or healthcare delivered via ITC or telecomunictions.

Vertical farming The growing of animals or plants in vertical buildings or skyscrapers, usually in urban environments.

Virtual currency Digital currency used primarily in computer gaming. Links with digital payments, micro-payments, stored value, embedded currency and mobile payments.

Virtual duplicate An object's virtual twin in cyberspace. Used to provide additional information. Links with augmented reality and cyber-twins.

VR Virtual Reality - a computer-simulated environment.

Web 2.0 A term often used to describe Web applications that help individuals to share information online, examples being sites such as Facebook and YouTube. Sometimes referred to as the participatory or conversational Web.

Web 3.0 The next stage of Web development, although the term causes much disagreement. Sometimes refers to the ability of search engines to answer complex questions. It can also refer to the personalized Web, semantic Web or the geo-tagging of information.

Web 4.0 Like Web 3.0 but immersive.

Index

Quercus Editions Ltd
Carmelite House
50 Victoria Embankment
London
EC4Y 0DZ

First published in 2012

A catalogue record of this book is available from the
British Library

UK and associated territories: ISBN 978 1 78087 159 2

Printed and bound in China

10 9 8 7 6 5 4 3 2

Acknowledgements
Thanks are due to a handful of people, especially
Corrina Fox and Matt Doyle who read early versions of
the manuscript and made some helpful suggestions.
Thanks are also due to Scott Martin, Martin Haigh,
David Balson, Ashley McKimm and Chris Evett, who
read sections and pointed me in the right direction
on a number of subjects, to Emma Heyworth-Dunn at
Quercus, and to Ali Moore, who polished the final text.
Last, but far from least, thanks to George, Nick and
Matt for the usual reasons.

Richard Watson

Picture credits
Diagram on page 138 copyright 2005 Karl F. MacDorman
and Takashi Minato. Permission is granted to copy,
distribute and/or modify this document under the terms
of the GNU Free Documentation License, Version 1.2.
Source: Wikimedia Commons.